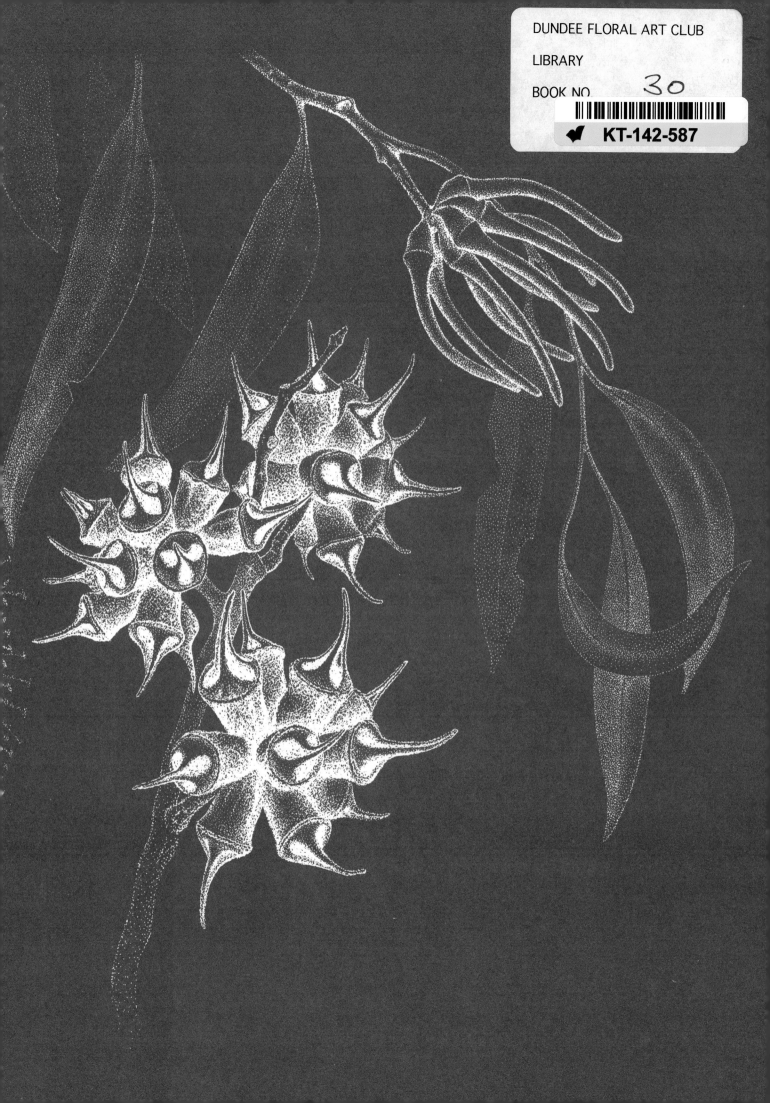

Australia's Wildflowers

Michael Morcombe

Australia's Wildflowers

Lansdowne

Lansdowne Press Pty Ltd
(a division of Paul Hamlyn Pty Ltd)
176 South Creek Road, Dee Why West, Australia 2099
First published 1970
Reprinted 1976
© Michael Morcombe 1970
SBN 7018 0340 1
Type set by Dudley E. King,
Linotypers, Melbourne, Vic 3000
Printed in Hong Kong
Endpapers Yate *(Eucalyptus cornuta)* Colour: yellow.
Occurrence: south-cost WA.
Flowering: Jan to Feb.

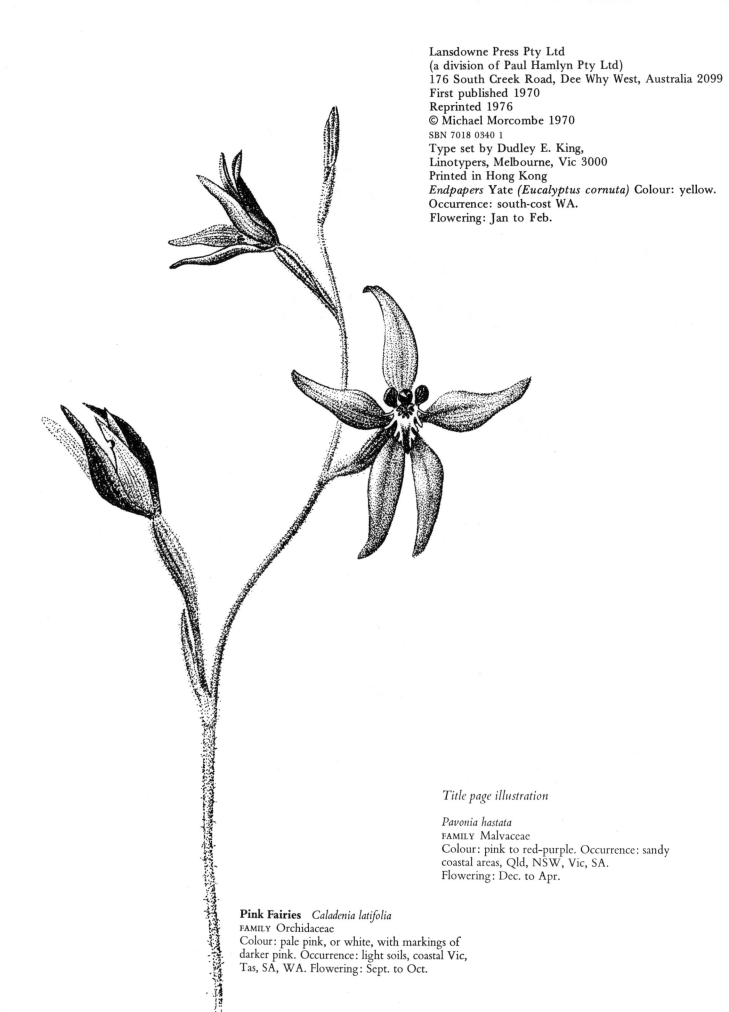

Title page illustration

Pavonia hastata
FAMILY Malvaceae
Colour: pink to red-purple. Occurrence: sandy
coastal areas, Qld, NSW, Vic, SA.
Flowering: Dec. to Apr.

Pink Fairies *Caladenia latifolia*
FAMILY Orchidaceae
Colour: pale pink, or white, with markings of
darker pink. Occurrence: light soils, coastal Vic,
Tas, SA, WA. Flowering: Sept. to Oct.

CONTENTS

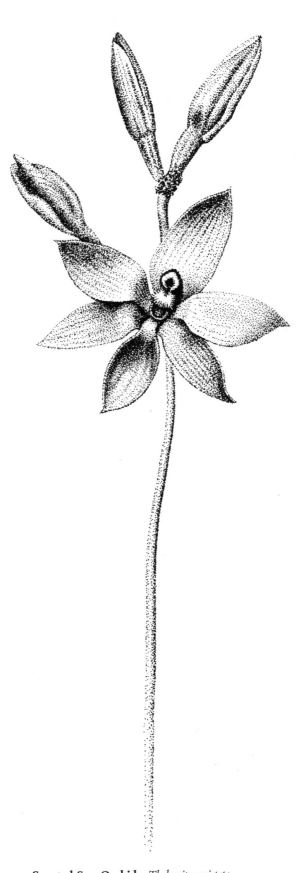

White Correa *Correa alba*
FAMILY Rutaceae
Colour: pure white. Occurrence: coastal south-
eastern Aust. Flowering: a long period,
particularly winter.

Scented Sun Orchid *Thelymitra aristata*
FAMILY Orchidaceae
Colour: blue, violet or mauve with orange tip
to column. Occurrence: all states.
Flowering: Sept. to Nov.

INTRODUCTION

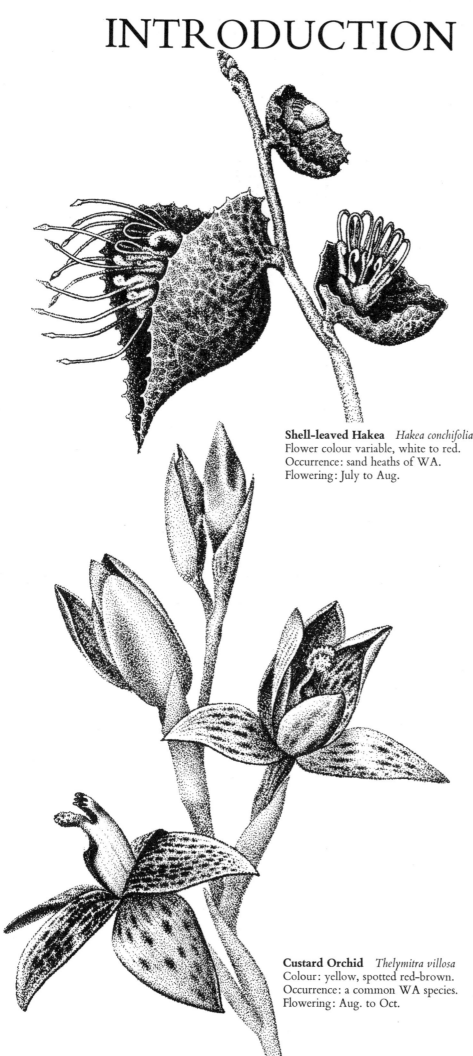

Shell-leaved Hakea *Hakea conchifolia*
Flower colour variable, white to red.
Occurrence: sand heaths of WA.
Flowering: July to Aug.

Custard Orchid *Thelymitra villosa*
Colour: yellow, spotted red-brown.
Occurrence: a common WA species.
Flowering: Aug. to Oct.

This book shows the Australian flora in its natural environment: Mountain Buttercups beside snowdrifts on Mt Kosciusko, Yellow Everlastings on the high volcanic ridges of the Warrumbungle Ranges, Parakeelya en masse across the red plains of the Centre, Lotus Lilies on a tropical lagoon, Yellow Hibiscus shrubs flowering on hill slopes overlooking islands of the Barrier Reef coastline, and Golden Kangaroo-paws on the sandplains of Western. Australia.

In this respect it is an endeavour to show an intrinsic quality of any indigenous flora—that it is a natural association, with all plant and animal species completely interdependent, evolved to meet the needs of the particular environment. Difficult as it is to protect individual species, the preservation of complete samples of our natural environment, with all its delicate ecological balances, presents even greater problems. Scenes such as shown in this book are becoming fewer as destructive exploitation of natural resources spreads even to the most remote areas.

In addition to showing Australian wildflowers in the natural bushland habitat, this book shows many species that are rare, or unique to certain localities, or of particular scientific interest, or common yet flamboyantly colourful. It will assist in the identification of many wildflowers likely to be seen around Australia.

Six natural regions are covered, encompassing the entire continent.

THE SOUTH is Australia's region of mountains, which reach their climax in the 7,000 ft peaks of the Snowy Mountains. While the lowland flora of this region holds much of interest, emphasis has been placed upon the alpine flora of the south-east and Tasmania because it is a feature not duplicated in other parts of Australia.

THE EAST COAST includes the flora of the Hawkesbury sandstone country around Sydney, and of the 'granite belt' country of south-east Queensland. This is an exceptionally rich flora, not only having a very great number of flowering plants, but also possessing such popular species as the Waratah, several species of Christmas Bell, Gymea Lily and Golden Glory Pea.

THE CENTRE is a region of red plains, red sand dunes, red gorges, extensive dry claypans and glaring white dry salt lakes—and of unexpected contrasts provided by the lush greenery of river gums, even palms, around pools and waterholes. It is only after a winter of exceptional rains that the centre reveals the full extent of its floral wealth. The bare earth beneath the mulga scrub becomes carpeted with the white, gold, pink and purple of

6

transient annuals. This pageantry lasts but a few weeks. Soon the earth is dry again, with only the scattered remnants of papery flowers in the red dust—and the hard seeds which must survive the centre's droughts, and months of scorching heat.

THE NORTH and NORTH-EAST are principally savannah-woodlands, where such species as the Tropical Woollybutt, *Eucalyptus miniata*, the Wild Cotton, *Cochlospermum gregorii*, and *Brachychiton paradoxus* occur. But a great deal of the botanical interest of these regions is centred upon the smaller areas taken up by rainforests, home of epiphytic orchids and ferns, and the lagoons and swamps where huge water-lilies, *Nelumbo* and *Nymphaea* often grow in profusion.

Finally, the 'wildflower state', or more specifically, the SOUTH-WEST, for the principal wildflower wealth of that huge state lies in its south-western vegetation province. During thousands of years of isolation from the eastern coast by deserts which stretch from the Great Australian Bight to the north-western coast, south-western flora developed many unique groups. Only there do we find the golden and bronzed dryandras, the many bizarre kangaroo-paws and the fiery *Nuytsia*.

The botanist J. D. Hooker wrote of the Australian flora:

'It contains more genera and species peculiar to its own areas, and fewer plants belonging to other parts of the world, than any other country of equal extent. About two-fifths of its genera, and upwards of seven-eighths of its species, are entirely confined to Australia.'

But although the majority of its species and many of its genera are endemic, the Australian flora is very much part of the world flora—the Australian plant families (with several minor exceptions) occur also in other countries. Those families that are most widely distributed in Australia are also the most widely distributed elsewhere. The distinctive quality of the Australian flora is principally at the level of genus and species. Over a long period of time, on this large, isolated island, a whole new spectrum of unique Australian species, and genera, has developed within the framework of those widespread families.

Several families contain an exceptional wealth of flowering trees, shrubs or small plants. Without any doubt the families Proteaceae, Myrtaceae and Mimosaceae very much set the character of the Australian bush, while the orchid family has many species that are of great interest. These families are therefore described in some detail, with special attention to several genera of particular interest.

FAMILY Orchidaceae

The distinguishing feature of this family is that the flowers, although of tremendously diverse shape, size and colour, have in common (and in this respect differ from other flowering plants) a structure known as the column. This is made up of united anthers, style and stigma, with the anthers being situated at the tip of the column. The pollen is waxy, and clustered into one or a number of pollen masses known as pollina. There are three sepals and three petals, the lower petal often being more or less modified in shape and colour, when it is referred to as the 'labellum'.

The orchid family is usually divided into two large groups, the epiphytes, which attach themselves to the surfaces of trees or boulders, and the ground or terrestrial orchids.

The epiphytes, which are not parasitic, include the many species of *Dendrobium*, *Cymbidium*, *Sarcochilus*, *Bulbophyllum*, *Vanda*, *Phalaenopsis*, and numerous other genera. They are for the most part confined to the humid tropical northern and eastern coasts.

The terrestrial orchids are a larger group, much more widely distributed through Australia. Among the numerically dominant genera are *Thelymitra*, *Caladenia*, *Diuris* and *Pterostylis*.

While the orchid family is widely distributed outside Australia, with many magnificent tropical species, the relatively small-flowered Australian orchids have always been a subject of considerable interest, both as wild flowers, and as subjects for horticulture.

FAMILY Proteaceae

Probably the family Proteaceae is responsible more than any other for the unique character of the Australian flora. The continent's south-western corner, with some 500 species, has a disproportionately large share of this family: of the total 37 Australian genera, four, including *Dryandra*, are endemic to the south-west, while *Banksia* and *Hakea* are richly represented. The family has almost 500 south-western species.

The flowers of the Proteaceae are comprised of four perianth segments, which in the bud stage form a tube sheathing the long style. The four stamens, often lacking filaments, are attached to the perianth segments, and in close contact with the stigma. At the time of flowering the perianth tube splits, the segments roll back, leaving the pollen on the stigma, to be carried away by birds or insects; in some genera the four stamens as well as the style are left protruding.

In many instances hundreds, even thousands of such small flowers are arranged on cylindrical, spherical or conical spikes or racemes, sometimes forming an inflorescence more than twelve inches in length.

7

Of the many genera in the family Proteaceae, the banksias, dryandras, grevilleas, hakeas, waratahs, isopogons, petrophilas, conospermums and lambertias together account for many of the best flowering trees and shrubs in the Australian bush.

The genus *Banksia*, commemorating Sir Joseph Banks, who collected the first specimens in 1770 at Botany Bay, has several species with flower spikes so large that they are conspicuous from a distance of several hundred yards—yet so finely detailed and patterned that they make fascinating close-up studies.

Each spike, which may grow to a length of eighteen inches (*Banksia grandis*), contains thousands of close-packed, spirally-arranged tiny flowers, every one a small tubular perianth that splits and rolls back to leave a long stiff straight, or sometimes hooked style to make part of the brush-like surface of the banksia spike. At the same time the texture and colour of the spike changes, with a band of colour, usually orange or yellow of pollen-tipped styles, spreading up the spike.

One of the most spectacular of the genus is *Banksia ashbyi*, a tree of the Western Australian sandplains. The long, slightly tapering cylindrical flower spikes, up to a foot in length, are deep rich cadmium yellow, turning orange as the flowers open. Held high on the tree these large fiery spikes make vivid contrast to the deep blue north-western skies.

For intricate detail more reminiscent of the finest work of a jeweller, silversmith or sculptor of miniatures in metal than of living flower, the crimson *Banksia occidentalis* must be one of the best of its genus. A close view is needed to reveal the finely incised lines of the developing rows of flowers on the vivid green small new spikes; or the complex detail of the fine stiff wire-like rows of burnished crimson looped styles arrayed up a spike about to come into flower.

Also in the Proteaceae, the genus *Dryandra*, with fifty-nine species found only in south-western Australia, has flowers clustered in heads, surrounded towards the base by encircling scale-like bracts. On some species (*Dryandra runcinata, D. proteoides, D. speciosa*) these bracts are the most prominent feature of the inflorescence, being generally of golden, bronzed or reddish tones. Other species (*D. stuposa, D. formosa, D. falcata*) have long stiff golden or bronzed styles and relatively inconspicuous bracts.

The genus *Grevillea*, containing some 250 endemic species, is found throughout Australia. Flowers are usually borne on rather loose open racemes, which are in some cases very large and showy. The seeds of almost all species are dropped when the thin-walled fruits split open soon after flowering is finished. In this respect the grevilleas differ from the otherwise very similar hakeas.

There are 130 to 140 species of *Hakea* in Australia. These range in size from trees to small shrubs. Flowers are usually on racemes or spikes, similar to those of the grevilleas. Fruits are thick, hard and woody, and remain on the shrub for months or years after flowering, splitting to release the seed usually only after a fire, or death of the shrub.

There are, in this large family, many other genera containing superb flowering shrubs or trees: *Telopea* (the four species of Waratah), *Isopogon* and *Petrophile* (rose cone bushes, drumsticks), *Conospermum* (smokebushes), *Lambertia*, and *Stenocarpus* (Wheel of Fire).

FAMILY Mimosaceae

Although the 'acacia family', Mimosaceae, is not exclusively Australian, it is on this continent that one of its genera, *Acacia*, has exploded into bewildering diversity of form and profusion of species.

The family has three Australian genera—*Acacia* (the wattles), *Albizia*, and *Neptunia*. Family characteristics include bacterial nodules on the roots (a feature shared with other legumes), alternate leaves (often bipinnate or reduced to phyllodes) and the fruit a pod (legume).

The numerically dominant Australian genus *Acacia* has approximately 600 species, with exceptionally wide distribution throughout the continent. Across vast areas of the semi-arid and arid interior Acacia scrub ('mulga') forms almost the entire woody vegetation.

Flowers of *Acacia* are regular and symmetrical, with five sepals, five petals, and are never solitary but collected together in round heads, or spikes which in turn may be arranged in racemes or pannicles. The stamens are extremely numerous, giving the flower heads their fluffy appearance.

Leaves are always divided, fernlike, being composed of many small leaflets—but more often than not the pinnate leaves are replaced soon after seedling stage by phyllodes. These modified leaf stalks, often leaf-like in appearance, may be needle-like, stiff and sharp, or flattened, with a great diversity of shapes, and much like ordinary leaves in general appearance (e.g. *Acacia celastrifolia*). Some species have winged stems which function as leaves.

In many cases the leaflessness is a modification for survival in an increasingly arid climate.

Many species bear flowers in such profusion that the foliage is all but concealed by the golden masses. *Acacia* seed germinates readily, growth is rapid, and it is possible to select from a wide variety of species that flower at different times of the year.

FAMILY Myrtaceae

With 51 Australian genera, including *Callistemon*, *Melaleuca*, *Kunzea*, *Verticordia*, *Calytrix*, *Darwinia* and *Eucalyptus*, this widely distributed family contains a great number of superb trees and shrubs. Family characteristics include leaves with small oil glands, flowers with five sepals that are united in their lower part into a calyx tube (often bell-shaped), five petals (modified in Eucalyptus) and numerous stamens that often form the most conspicuous part of the flower.

The genus *Eucalyptus* dominates the Australian landscape and the Australian flora. It contains about 450 distinct species, and is rivalled numerically and in universality of distribution only by the wattles.

In size the eucalypts range from mallees with a mature height of four or five feet to giants more than three hundred feet tall. They may be found above 6,000 feet on the south-east highlands, at the very uppermost limit of tree growth (Snow Gum, *E. niphophila*); they grow in the waterlogged soils around swamps, the margins of billabongs and on river flood-plains (River Gum, *E. camaldulensis*), and they may be found on the most barren rocky ranges of the arid interior (Ghost Gum, *E. papuana*).

The genus is distinguished from all others by the flowers, which have neither sepals nor petals. Petals are fused together to form a bud cap, or operculum, which covers the stamens in the bud, and falls to permit their unfolding.

Often this operculum is coloured, and sometimes decoratively ribbed. The Ilyarrie, *Eucalyptus erythrocorys*, has a crimson, deeply convoluted operculum that falls away to reveal yellow stamens; the Coral Gum, *E. torquata*, has an orange-red, deeply ribbed operculum that terminates in a long slender point (i.e. rostrate); the Goldfields Blackbutt, *E. lesouefii* has an orange-yellow ribbed operculum; Kingsmill's Mallee, *E. kingsmillii*, has a large, rostrate, sharply ribbed red to yellow-green operculum, and the Bushy Yate, *E. lehmanni*, has a globular cluster of flowers from which radiate long slender tapering tubular bud caps of a reddish brown colour. Other species have caps that are conical, hemispherical, smooth, warty, glaucous or glabrous—the great diversity of caps makes them an important aid to the identification of the eucalypts.

Also useful in identification is the bark, which may be persistent or deciduous. The persistent bark may be soft and short-fibred, or hard, or rough and furrowed. The deciduous bark, which is shed annually much as deciduous trees shed their leaves, is mainly of three kinds: It may be soft and brittle, falling away in short, irregular, almost fibre-less flakes; or hard, long-fibred, stripping away in broad thick bands up to several feet long; or it may be thin, finely fibred, shredding away in ribbons which may be very long.

Those eucalypts which have smooth bark are generally known as gums, but if there is a dark rough collar of old bark around the lower trunk the trees are commonly given such names as blackbutt, woollybutt. Trees with long-fibred barks are known as stringy-barks, while many other trees have their own distinctive barks—the peppermints, scaly-barks, boxes, bloodwoods, ashes, and scribbly gums.

Botanists sometimes classify eucalypts by characteristics of the anthers—the tiny pollen-making cells at the tip of each filament of the flower. In this case details of anther attachment to the filament (may be versatile, sub-versatile, adnate), shape of the anther (cordate, ovate, oblong, etc.) and shape of the openings through which pollen is released (slit, pore) are the distinguishing criteria.

Many eucalypts have colourful flowers, but the vast majority are white or creamy. Most of the colourful species show colour variations (from intense hues to pale tints or white) or hybridize to produce colour variations. This can make identification by colour unreliable, and makes colour an unpredictable factor when growing some species from seed. (Propagation from cuttings is very difficult.)

There are also a great many differences within the genus regarding leaf shape, size and surface, while the fruits, 'gumnuts', vary enormously in shape, size and botanical features such as valve structure.

Habit of growth, however, is probably the most conspicuous variable within this huge genus. Some invariably grow as trees, with a single columnar trunk which does not branch until high above the ground. Others possess a lignotuber—a swollen mass of woody tissue just beneath the ground. This contains a great many dormant buds, so that these eucalypts normally, as a characteristic habit of growth, send up many slender little stems, and have the power of regeneration from the lignotuber after fire; such species are known as mallees, and are most widespread in semi-arid areas.

While this book shows many of Australia's native flowers, its purpose must also emphasise that this flora is fast disappearing as destruction of the natural environment accelerates. In the not-too-distant future the wildflowers shown here will be found growing only in national parks and reserves set aside for the conservation of flora and fauna. These protected areas are as yet most inadequate for the conservation and recreational roles they will be required to play as Australia's population grows, and the remaining bushland is bulldozed away.

MICHAEL MORCOMBE

1970

9

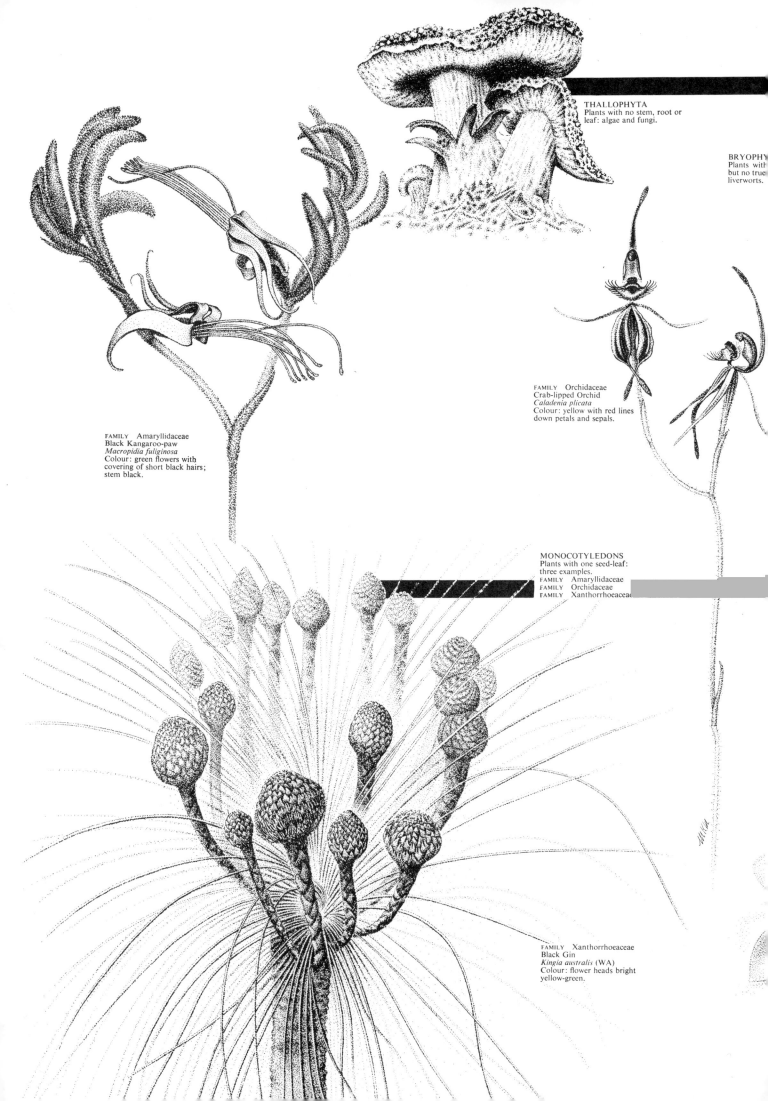

THALLOPHYTA
Plants with no stem, root or
leaf: algae and fungi.

BRYOPHY
Plants with
but no true
liverworts.

FAMILY   Orchidaceae
Crab-lipped Orchid
Caladenia plicata
Colour: yellow with red lines
down petals and sepals.

FAMILY   Amaryllidaceae
Black Kangaroo-paw
Macropidia fuliginosa
Colour: green flowers with
covering of short black hairs;
stem black.

MONOCOTYLEDONS
Plants with one seed-leaf:
three examples.
FAMILY   Amaryllidaceae
FAMILY   Orchidaceae
FAMILY   Xanthorrhoeaceae

FAMILY   Xanthorrhoeaceae
Black Gin
Kingia australis (WA)
Colour: flower heads bright
yellow-green.

THE PLANT KINGDOM

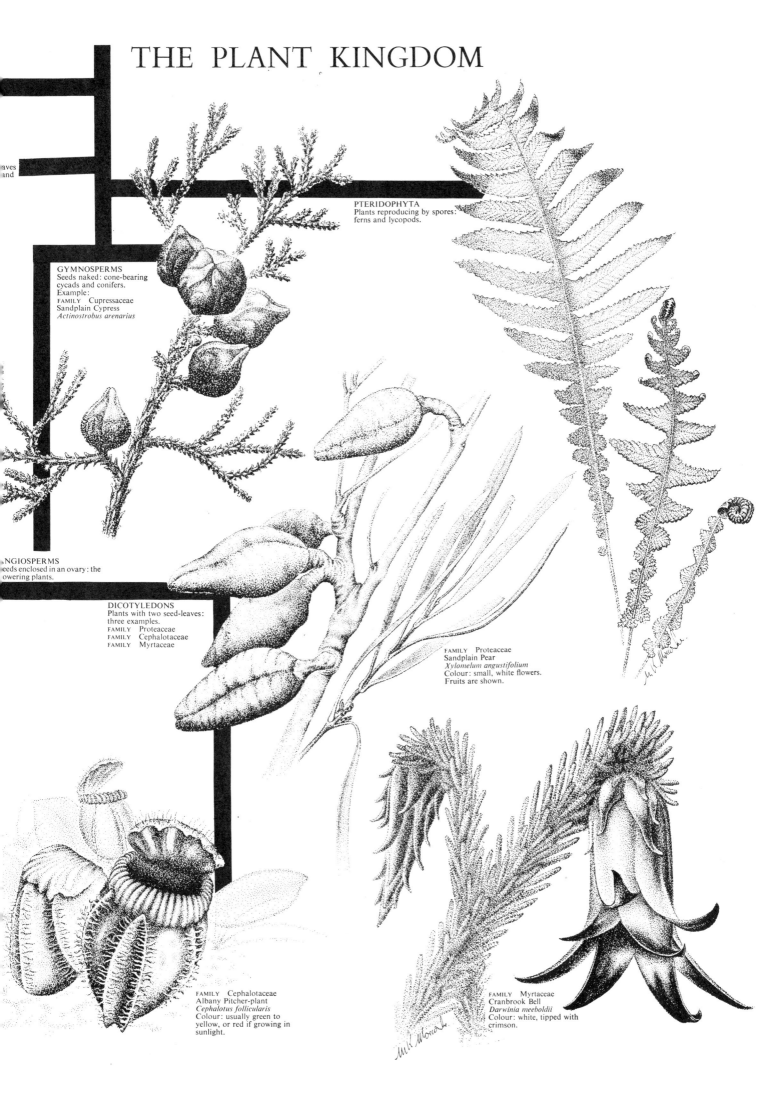

aves
and

PTERIDOPHYTA
Plants reproducing by spores:
ferns and lycopods.

GYMNOSPERMS
Seeds naked: cone-bearing
cycads and conifers.
Example:
FAMILY Cupressaceae
Sandplain Cypress
Actinostrobus arenarius

NGIOSPERMS
eeds enclosed in an ovary: the
owering plants.

DICOTYLEDONS
Plants with two seed-leaves:
three examples.
FAMILY Proteaceae
FAMILY Cephalotaceae
FAMILY Myrtaceae

FAMILY Proteaceae
Sandplain Pear
Xylomelum angustifolium
Colour: small, white flowers.
Fruits are shown.

FAMILY Cephalotaceae
Albany Pitcher-plant
Cephalotus follicularis
Colour: usually green to
yellow, or red if growing in
sunlight.

FAMILY Myrtaceae
Cranbrook Bell
Darwinia meeboldii
Colour: white, tipped with
crimson.

PART I
THE
SOUTH

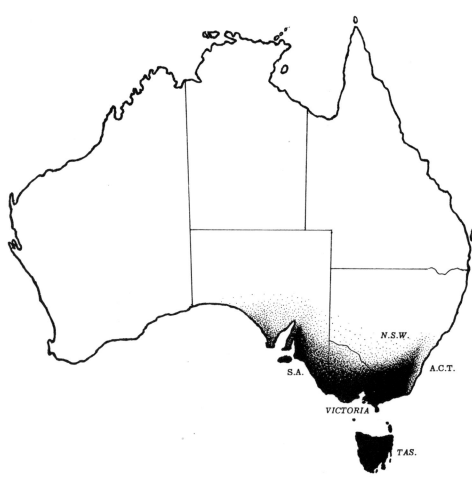

The Great Dividing Range in New South Wales and Victoria owes its present altitude to mighty movements in the earth's crust during late Pliocene times—two to three million years ago. This orogeny is known as the 'Kosciusko Uplift' because it reached a climax in the region of Mt Kosciusko where several peaks still exceed 7,000 ft. and are covered with snow for about half the year. Streams were rejuvenated by the uplift, and in the succeeding Pleistocene period heavy rainfall caused much natural erosion throughout the ranges. There is really no marked discontinuity in mountainous country from southern Victoria through eastern New South Wales and on into North Queensland; but, for this study, the term 'South-eastern Highlands' is applicable to all terrain of greater elevation than 2,000 ft., stretching from the Hunter and Goulburn River valleys (NSW) to the Grampians (Vic). Tasmania is included as an outlier of this highland system, but not so the Mt Lofty and Flinders Ranges in South Australia.

Within the tract thus defined at least 2,000 species of native flowering plants and ferns may be found, associated with such diverse rock types as: hard sandstones, shales and slates, granodiorite, various volcanics (basalt, rhyolite, etc.) of several ages, smaller amounts of limestone, some conglomerate and quartzite. At lower altitudes, geological structure has a significant influence on the composition of the vegetation, but around and above 4,000 ft. it is climate rather than geology that controls the plant formations. Heights above 4,500 ft. in Tasmania and above 6,000 ft. on the mainland are inimical to all tree growth, and its place is taken over by low alpine shrubberies, herbfields, grassy meadows or mossy bogs.

The richest display of flowers is to be seen at the two extremities—ranges of the isolated Grampians in western Victoria and the high dissected country on and north of the Blue Mountains in New South Wales. In both areas the dominant rock formation is sandstone of Upper Palaeozoic age (some 200–250 million years ago); spectacular scarps, bluffs and gorges provide a magnificent backdrop to the interesting floras which contain many endemic species. Ten plants, including four kinds of buttercups, are endemic on the Kosciusko Plateau, chiefly around the summit area (6,500–7,300 ft.). In Tasmania 200 species, about 16 percent of the total vascular flora, are endemic and most of these unique plants are confined to mountain country with high precipitation.

Lofty alpine moors undoubtedly provide the most colourful and, in many ways, most interesting communities of highland plants. More than 200 species are restricted to these almost or quite treeless tracts and, when certain

12

lowland plants do appear in the alps they usually have larger and more vividly coloured blooms. Here the seasons for growth and flowering are short (December to March), and a rigorous environment—strong winds, freezing winter temperatures and high insolation during summer—has brought about some very distinctive modifications in life-form. Where boulders are present, shrubs may hug closely to their surfaces like mats or unilateral espaliers, for instance the alpine form of Tree Violet, Mountain Plum Pine, Mountain Baeckea and Yellow Kunzea. The tufted or rosetted habit is frequent, e.g. in numerous alpine daisies, buttercups, plantains, etc. Other plants form carpets or cushions only a few inches high, their tiny leafy shoots so densely packed that one may step on the 'cushion' without depressing or damaging it in any way. Cushion plants are particularly well developed on Tasmanian mountain plateaux, and sometimes several unrelated species—in such genera as *Donatia*, *Dracophyllum*, *Pterygopappus* and *Ewartia*—will grow tightly intermingled in the same colony. Intricate mingling of separate plants is quite conspicuous in the complex community of a sphagnum bog where sedges, heaths, sundews, orchids, ferns, various mosses and hepatics all occur together in a tangled mass.

Some alpine flowers come into bloom very early, and the beautiful Marsh-marigold, *Caltha introloba*, may actually expand its white petals in little grottoes of ice at the melting edge of snowdrifts. Strong perfumes are exhaled by some alpines, notably the matted *Stackhousia pulvinaris*. *Caltha*, *Anemone*, *Geum*, *Seseli*, the ferns *Botrychium* and *Cystopteris* are all typically temperate genera of the northern hemisphere, and their reappearance in the Antipodes has not yet been adequately explained. The genera *Phyllachne*, *Donatia*, *Ourisia*, *Pernettya* and *Gunnera* are each restricted in the Australian region to a single small Tasmanian species, yet they occur again along the Andean chain of South America. This ancient link with America by means of the Antarctic is also well exemplified in such woody genera as *Araucaria*, *Nothofagus*, *Lomatia* and *Fuchsia* (New Zealand but not Australia).

As one climbs higher into the mountains, members of the vast daisy group, *Compositae*, become more and more conspicuous in the flora until, on the higher alps, they exceed numerically the species in any other plant family. Thus, on the windswept heights of Kosciusko, we find impressive sheets of marguerite-like Silver Daisies, *Celmisia*, masses of golden Billy-buttons, *Craspedia*, several kinds of papery 'everlastings' (*Helichrysum* and *Helipterum* species), cudweeds, *Gnaphalium*, daisy-bushes, *Olearia*, smaller herbaceous daisies, *Brachycome*, and many others, making unforgettable landscapes features in summertime.

At the upper limit of tree growth, shrubberies and sub-alpine woodlands of stunted but often very picturesque eucalypts (chiefly *Eucalyptus pauciflora* var. *alpina*, Snow Gum, on the mainland but also *E. coccifera*, *E. urnigera* and *E. vernicosa* in Tasmania) appear; these may occur also in the shelter of rocks and crags at elevations above the normal tree-line. The only species of *Acacia* in this region is the bushy *A. alpina*, but taller *A. obliquinervia*, Mountain Hickory, sometimes enters the lower limit of Snow Gum woodlands. With decreasing altitude, the hardy dwarfed eucalypts merge into taller woodlands and forests dominated by *E. delegatensis*, *E. dalrympleana*, *E. nitens*, etc. The magnificent, fragrantly aromatic Alpine Ash or 'Woollybutt', *E. delegatensis*, is an important timber tree that can attain heights of more than 200 ft. Often forming extensive pure stands, with a scrubless grassy forest floor, it occupies chiefly the zone between 3,000 and 4,000 ft. in Victoria and New South Wales but may descend to 1,000 ft. in cooler parts of Tasmania. The most impressive tree of this altitudinal range in the Blue Mountains is Blue Ash, *E. oreades*, which is straight-boled and occasionally reaches heights of 120 ft.

The mallee habit in eucalypts is usually associated with semi-arid lands of low relief, where sand-ridges or highly calcareous soils predominate. However, several small montane species in eastern Victoria and New South Wales have adopted this 'whipstick' manner of growth, viz. *E. kybeanensis*, *E. glaucescens*, *E. stricta* and *E. apiculata*. Underlying rock structure may sometimes induce normally taller trees with single trunks to assume a reduced and many-stemmed mallee form; this occurs with the two mallees *E. pauciflora* and *E. stellulata* which intermingle with typical mountain mallees, *E. kybeanensis* and *E. glaucescens*, on the exposed north-eastern edge of Nunniong Plateau in East Gippsland.

Many species of eucalypt enter into the composition of montane forests between 2,000 and 3,000 ft. A very widespread alliance is that of *E. obliqua*, Messmate, and *E. cypellocarpa*, Mountain Grey Gum, with a varying understorey of *Acacia melanoxylon*, Blackwood, *A. dealbata*, Silver Wattle, *Pomaderris aspera*, *Prostanthera lasianthos*, *Olearia argophylla*, *Helichrysum dendroideum*, *Bedfordia salicina* and/or other small trees. Here too, on the deep rich soils of cool mountain valleys, preferably with southern or easterly aspect, is the optimum habitat of the world's tallest flowering plant, *E. regnans*, Mountain Ash. This gigantic eucalypt towers occasionally to more than 300 ft., and in southern Tasmania (near Maydena) a 322-foot specimen still flourishes.

Except at the blackish butt, its pale greenish-grey bark is quite smooth, decorticating in long ribbons; trees are relatively shallow-rooting, easily killed by fire and do not coppice when cut down. Indigenous only to Tasmania, southern and eastern Victoria, *E. regnans* is replaced in the highlands of New South Wales by the related but fibrous-barked *E. fastigata*, Brown Barrel or 'Cut-tail'. The Myrtle Beech, *Nothofagus cunninghamii*, sometimes associates with Mountain Ash along the deep sheltered valleys of southern Victoria and especially Tasmania where it may dominate the forest in areas of higher rainfall. This evergreen beech is a handsome tree, of quite venerable mien when old and characteristically draped with epiphytic lichens, mosses and ferns; at 3,000–4,000 ft. it becomes much reduced in size, and on Tasmanian mountain-tops is succeeded by the curious little deciduous beech, *Nothofagus gunnii*—brilliantly golden in late autumn.

All through these mountain forests of taller trees, wherever rainfall exceeds 35 inches, fern gullies are of frequent occurrence. Shelter, abundant moisture and equable, microclimatic conditions encourage a luxuriant growth of ferns—from tall tree-ferns (20–40 ft. in height) to tiny epiphytic filmy ferns—with a rich attendant flora of shade-loving herbs, mosses, lichens and fungi. On wetter gully floors the spicily aromatic Southern Sassafras, *Atherosperma moschatum*, is a trim little tree of regular conical shape; its white scented flowers appear on the underside of branchlets during mid-winter. Several tall creepers may also be present in the fern-gully formation, e.g. Clematis, Purple Apple-berry, Twining Silk-pod and Wonga Vine, while the climbing Forest Wire-grass often forms dense fringing entanglements. An interesting grass is *Dryopoa dives*, Giant Mountain Grass, which looks like a titanic oat plant and may grow to 15 ft. in height. Jungle growth of sub-tropical origin may occasionally intrude into higher mountain gullies, but it is normally confined to warmer near-coastal situations in eastern New South Wales and far eastern Victoria; none extends to Tasmania.

Drier, more open forests of stringybarks, peppermints and a few box-barked eucalypts occupy enormous areas on the mainland foot-hills below 2,000 ft., sometimes encroaching along ranges above this altitude, especially on exposed northerly and westerly slopes. Numerous wattles and other bright-flowered leguminous shrubs, as well as many heaths, daisy-bushes and quaint orchids are to be found in this formation. Species of riparian shrubs or small trees, notably *Lomatia myricoides*, *Gynatrix* (Plagianthus) *pulchella*, *Leptospermum grandifolium* and *L. phylicoides* (Burgan), inhabit many stream banks in the highlands of New South Wales and Victoria, while in Tasmania

endemic species of *Eucryphia*, Leatherwood, and *Anodopetalum biglandulosum*, 'Horizontal', seem to occupy the same ecological niche.

One of the most remarkable Tasmanian plants is the giant, palm-like heath, *Richea pandanifolia*, 'Pandani', the slender trunk of which may occasionally rise to 40 ft., its densely crowded leaves, in a terminal mop, are commonly 3–4 ft. long. Mountain plateaux of Tasmania also have a profusion of coloured berries in season, many of them belonging to the heath family; and there are several very interesting endemic conifers of the higher mountains—in the genera *Athrotaxis*, *Dacrydium*, *Phyllocladus*, *Microstrobus*, *Microcachrys* and *Diselma*, all confined (within the Common-wealth) to Tasmania excepting *Microstrobus* which has a single extremely localized species in the Blue Mountains, NSW.

The three waratahs, *Telopea speciosissima* (NSW), *T. oreades* (Vic, NSW) and *T. truncata* (Tas) may ascend to elevations of 3,000–4,000 ft. and are among Australia's most arrestingly beautiful flowers; *T. speciosissima* is the gazetted floral emblem for New South Wales. Victoria's emblem, the pink form of Common Heath, *Epacris impressa*, is to be found now and again above 2,000 ft., but it is of much more frequent occurrence in the foothill country and on coastal heathlands, with stunted outliers in the Little Desert.

J. H. Willis,
Assistant Government Botanist,
Royal Botanic Gardens,
Melbourne, Vic.

James H. Willis, B.Sc., Dip. For. (Creswick), was born at Oakleigh, Victoria, in 1910. He was educated at Melbourne Boys' High School, entering the Victorian School of Forestry at Creswick in 1928. Following seven years field experience he joined the National Herbarium of Victoria in 1937. He is now Assistant Government Botanist in Victoria. Mr Willis is a member of the Royal Society of Victoria, the National Trust of Australia, the Field Naturalists' Club of Victoria, the Native Plants Preservation Society, the Australian Conservation Foundation and the David G. Stead Memorial Wildlife Research Foundation of Australia.

Mr Willis has published a number of books, including the major Handbook to Plants in Victoria Vol. 1 (1962), Botanical Pioneers of Victoria (1949), Victorian Toadstools and Mushrooms (3rd ed. 1963), and was a joint author of Flowers and Plants of Victoria (1969), and more than 200 articles in various scientific and semi-scientific journals. In the nine volumes of the Australian Encyclopaedia (1958) he contributed 452 botanical and biographical entries. He was awarded the Australian Natural History medallion of 1960.

Banded Greenhood *Pterostylis vittata*
FAMILY Orchidaceae
Colour: reddish-brown flowers heavily banded in green and white. Occurrence: south-eastern and south-western Aust. Flowering: July to Sept.

14

ALFRED NATIONAL PARK (VIC)
SE on Princes Hwy, 300 m. E of Melbourne.

Mountainous, forested region, containing some of the most southerly occurrences of sub-tropical rainforest; epiphytic orchids, many ferns and vines.

ALLIGATOR GORGE NATIONAL PARK (SA)
Lower Flinders Ranges, 83 m. N of Adelaide via Wilmington.

Rugged ranges, open dry-sclerophyll forest with native Cypress Pines and *Casuarina*. Low scrub undergrowth has many spring wildflowers.

BAW BAW ALPINE RESERVE (VIC)
Forests Commission of Victoria. On Mt Baw Baw, Victorian Alps.

Mountain summit and high plains (to 5,127 ft), alpine vegetation, summer wildflowers.

BELAIR NATIONAL PARK (SA)
On Mt Lofty Ranges, 8 m. S of Adelaide.

Hilly, with dry-sclerophyll forest and savannah woodland; wildflowers in spring months.

BEN LOMOND NATIONAL PARK (TAS)
NE between Launceston and St Marys.

A high (to 5,160 ft) dolerite plateau, alpine vegetation on the heights, wet-sclerophyll forests on the slopes.

BILLIATT NATIONAL PARK (SA)
E area, between townships of Peebinga and Mindarie.

Sandy country with mallee vegetation; many wildflowers, especially of family Compositae, in early spring months.

BULGA NATIONAL PARK (VIC)
S Gippsland, between Yarram and Traralgon, 120 m. SE from Melbourne.

Strzlecki Ranges; contains sample of original south Gippsland temperate rainforest and wet-sclerophyll forest. Mountain Ash, many tree ferns.

CHURCHILL NATIONAL PARK (VIC)
20 m. E of Melbourne.

Sclerophyll forest on ranges, wildflowers in spring months.

CLELAND NATIONAL PARK (SA)
Mt Lofty ranges, to summit, overlooking Adelaide.

Dry sclerophyll forest, spring wildflowers.

CRADLE MTN–LAKE ST CLAIR NATIONAL PARK (TAS)
Central-eastern highlands.

Mountainous, with peaks above 5,000 ft. Alpine vegetation on heights, with wildflowers such as Alpine Boronia (*Boronia rhomboidea*), cushion plants such as *Dracophyllum minimum*, the Tasmanian Christmas Bell (*Blandfordia punicea*), and the Red Mountain Berry (*Cyathodes parvifolia*).

FERNTREE GULLY NATIONAL PARK (VIC)
22 m. E of Melbourne.

Wet sclerophyll forest on Dandenong Ranges, ferns in gullies.

FERRIES-MCDONALD NATIONAL PARK (SA)
Lower Murray SW from Murray Bridge.

Sandplain with mallee-broombush scrub.

FRASER NATIONAL PARK (VIC)
On western shores of Lake Eildon, 97 m. NE from Melbourne

Natural bush species, including many flowering plants, are being allowed to regenerate on former grazed land beside Lake Eildon.

FRENCHMAN'S CAP NATIONAL PARK (TAS)
SW Tas, S of Lyell Hwy, between Derwent Bridge and Queenstown.

A very high peak in a wilderness alpine region; alpine vegetation on heights, temperate rainforest and wet-sclerophyll forests at lower levels, swampy button-grass plains.

GRAMPIANS WONDERLAND FOREST PARK (VIC)
Forests Commission of Victoria. W Vic, near Halls Gap, 14 m. SW of Stawell.

Sandstone ranges with outstanding scenery. The heights carry scrubby vegetation, heathlands, and a number of species endemic to the district, or to western Vic: *Asterolasia phebalioides*, *Grevillea dimorpha*, *G. aquifolium*, and *Pultenaea patellifolia*.

HAMBIDGE NATIONAL PARK (SA)
Central Eyre Peninsula 10 m. E from Lock.

Sandridges and plains with mallee and heath vegetation, best in early spring.

HARTZ MOUNTAINS NATIONAL PARK (TAS)
S Tas, 8 m. W of Geeveston.

Mountain plateau up to 4,113 ft; alpine vegetation on heights, temperate rainforest and wetsclerophyll forests on the slopes.

HATTAH LAKES NATIONAL PARK (VIC)
Murray R. overflow lakes area, NW Vic.

Sandy mallee country; good displays of inland wildflowers early spring.

HINCKS NATIONAL PARK (SA)
On Eyre Peninsula between Lock and Cummins.

Sandplain and stabilized dunes; mallee, mallee-broombush and heathland associations.

KINGLAKE NATIONAL PARK (VIC)
Approx. 40 m. NE of Melbourne.

Forested ranges, with tall gums.

KOSCIUSKO NATIONAL PARK (NSW)
On the Snowy Mountains, SW from Canberra.

High plateaux with glaciated landforms and extensive winter snowfields; altitude range within the park exceeds 6,000 ft, giving clearly-defined vegetation zones. Alpine on summits, wet and dry sclerophyll forests, temperate woodlands. Park's most interesting species are the alpine flowers that appear on the heights as snows recede in December and January, e.g. *Ranunculus anemoneus*, *R. muelleri*, *Podolepis jaceoides*, and *Celmissia longifolia*.

LIND NATIONAL PARK (VIC)
E Gippsland, on Princes Hwy between Orbost and Cann R.

Mountainous, dense subtropical rainforest, dry eucalypt forest, habitat of the Gippsland Waratah, *Telopea oreades*.

LITTLE DESERT NATIONAL PARK (VIC)
Central-western Vic near Kiata.

Sandplain and mallee country, many sandplain wildflowers, including species endemic to western Vic.

LYELL HWY RESERVE (TAS)
W highlands, alongside hwy between Queenstown and Derwent R.

Extensive temperate rainforests, with Antarctic Beech (*Nothofagus*), Sassafras, and several conifers; also stands of tall eucalypts.

MALLACOOTA NATIONAL PARK (VIC)
Near NSW border, far eastern Vic.

An ocean inlet, occupying a drowned river valley; surrounding sclerophyll forest is quite rich in flowering plants.

MT BARROW NATIONAL PARK (TAS)
NE Tas.

The summit of Mt Barrow, altitude 4,644 ft; alpine wildflowers in summer months.

MT BUFFALO NATIONAL PARK (VIC)
Mountains of NE Vic, 200 m. from Melbourne by Ovens Hwy.

A mountain plateau, alpine flora on the 'high plains' (heaths, peaty areas) and eucalypt forests below 4,500 ft.

MT BULLER ALPINE RESERVE (VIC)
Forests Commission of Victoria, W Vic Alps.

Mountain summit area, with alpine vegetation, wildflowers (summer).

MT FIELD NATIONAL PARK (TAS)
SW, overlooking Derwent Valley.

High plateau, peaks to 4,721 ft. Alpine vegetation on the heights, wet sclerophyll forest (with big gums) and temperate rainforest on the slopes.

MT RICHMOND NATIONAL PARK (VIC)
Near SW coast, 20 m. W of Portland.

Sandy soils of Mt Richmond (745 ft) support approx. 450 species of flowering plants, including some 50 species of orchids.

SOUTH-WEST NATIONAL PARK (TAS)
Includes former Lake Pedder N.P., and reaches to south coast of Tas. Access relatively difficult.

An extensive area dominated by mountain peaks. Swampy buttongrass plains, temperate rainforests.

TARRA VALLEY NATIONAL PARK (VIC)
S Gippsland, between Traralgon and Yarram.

In a valley of the Strzlecki Ranges; a sample of original temperate rainforest and wet sclerophyll forest with tall gums and treefern forests.

TIDBINBILLA FAUNA AND FLORA RESERVE (ACT)
Upper Tidbinbilla Valley.

Forested ranges reaching 5,100 ft; trees include Candlebarks, Broad-leaf Peppermint, Ribbon (or Manna) Gum, Narrow-leaf Peppermint, Alpine Ash, Mountain Gum.

WILSONS PROMONTORY NATIONAL PARK (VIC)
Southernmost tip of the Australian mainland, 140 m. SE from Melbourne.

A hilly peninsula with forest and heathlands; wide variety of wildflowers.

WINGAN INLET NATIONAL PARK (VIC)
On E Gippsland coast, 330 m. E of Melbourne.

Rainforest vegetation bordering river.

WYPERFELD NATIONAL PARK (VIC)
NW, 280 m. from Melbourne.

Sandhill and mallee country; 300 plant species, wildflowers of late winter, early spring are a major attraction.

Common Heath *Epacris impressa*
FAMILY Epacridaceae
Victoria's floral emblem, flowering in Wilson's Promontory National Park. It is a slender, wiry little shrub, with small rigid sharp leaves. Occurs in NSW, Vic, SA, Tas, on coastal heath, mountains to 4,000 ft, and dry mallee. Flowering time is May to Nov.

16

Grass Triggerplant *Stylidium graminifolium*
FAMILY Stylidiaceae
Growing in forest on the lower slopes of the
south-eastern Highlands, these triggerplants lift
their flower spikes on tall stems, a contrast to
the more stunted alpine specimens. This widespread species (Qld to Tas) is a perennial, with
long stiff narrow leaves. Flowering time is Dec.
to Feb.

Common Correa *Correa reflexa*
FAMILY Rutaceae
A variable species, with woolly-surfaced tubular
flowers, yellow-green to crimson; the 8 stamens,
tipped with large yellow anthers, protrude
from the tube, which has 4 outward-curved
lobes. Leaves may be heart-shaped, rounded or
oblong, with rough-hairy surface. This slender
little shrub occurs in a wide variety of habitats
from mountain forests to dry mallee scrub, Vic,
Tas, SA, NSW. Flowering time is May to Nov.

Alpine Rice-Flower *Pimelea alpina*
FAMILY Thymelaeaceae
A shrub to 3 ft, or often prostrate. Leaves
oblong to oblong-lanceolate, opposite, and
rather crowded towards the flowering stem-tips
leaves and stem glaucous. Flowers are pink,
sometimes white. Occurs on alpine heathlands
and in sub-alpine woodlands of southern NSW
and south-eastern Vic. Flowering time is Dec.
to Jan.

Tasmanian Waratah *Telopea truncata*
FAMILY Proteaceae
Tasmania's one waratah species is an erect, or
sometimes spreading shrub 5 to 10 ft tall, with
comparatively flattened (truncate) flower heads.
Leaves are alternate, 2 to 4 in. long, oblanceolate
to obovate, margins entire and often rolled
inwards, and with inconspicuous vein pattern.
Flowers are clustered in rather flat heads of
approx. 2 in. diameter, scarlet, or rarely yellow.
Widespread in wet mountainous regions,
endemic to Tas. Flowering time is Dec. to Mar.

Golden Guinea-Flower *Hibbertia procumbens*
FAMILY Dilleniaceae
A small procumbent shrub which forms a green
mat of radiating branches. Leaves are linear,
¼-in. long. Flowers are solitary, terminal,
brilliant orange-yellow and of quite large size.
In Tas it occurs on heathlands from coast to
mountain plateaux; extends also to Vic.
Flowering time is Aug. to Feb.

Red Mountain Berry *Cyathodes parvifolia*
FAMILY Epacridaceae
Found only in Tas, this small shrub (2 to 4 ft)
grows on rocky slopes of mountains and high
plateaux. Leaves are tiny, prickly, ¼ to ½-in.
long, green above, grey beneath. Flowers are
bell-shaped, borne in leaf-axils. Plants are of
two types: one bush produces only pollen, fails
to set seed, the other type fails to mature its
pollen, but if cross-pollinated will set seed.
Flowers Sept. to Dec. Berries Nov. to Feb.

Grass Triggerplant   *Stylidium graminifolium*
FAMILY Stylidiaceae
The filaments of the flower's 2 stamens are united to the long bent style to form a sensitive column that is normally arched back until its tip is below and between the petals; when touched near the base this pollen-tipped column rapidly springs across to dab the insect with pollen, or to receive pollen, hence the name triggerplants. It then slowly returns to the ready position. Flowering time is Dec. to Feb.

Hoary Sunray   *Helipterum albicans* var. *incanum*
FAMILY Compositae
The tall thin flower stems and the leaves of this alpine perennial are densely covered with fine woolly-white hairs. The species varies considerably from place to place, and has several forms. In the Australian Alps the Hoary Sunray most often has golden bracts; this variety, *incanum*, photographed in Tasmania, has white bracts and stems. Flowering time is Dec. to Mar.

Tasmanian Christmas Bell   *Blandfordia punice*
FAMILY Liliaceae
This *Blandfordia* is endemic to western Tasmania differing from the four mainland species in that the stamens are attached above the middle of the bell-shaped perianth tube, and the leaf margins are finely crenulate. Its orange-red flowers, about $1\frac{1}{2}$ in. long, are narrow, expanding towards the 6 spreading perianth lobes; alternate lobes are edged yellow. Flowering time is Oct. to Mar.

A Tea-Tree   *Leptospermum scoparium*
FAMILY Myrtaceae
A widespread shrub occurring in Vic, Tas, NSW, Qld and SA. Flowers may be white or pink, and up to $\frac{3}{4}$-in. diameter. The leaves are stiff, sharply pointed and slightly concave on the upper surface. Propagation can be from seed or cuttings. Flowering time is Oct. to Feb.

Dusty Daisy-Bush
           Olearia phlogopappa var. *subrepanda*
FAMILY Compositae
An alpine variant of the Dusty Daisy-bush with leaves hoary-grey above, and finely woolly-surfaced, yellow-grey on the undersurface, giving the whole shrub a grey dust-laden appearance. Leaves are finely toothed, and about $\frac{1}{2}$-in. long. Flowers are borne in solitary terminal heads. Occurs south-eastern alpine regions. Flowers Dec. to Feb.

Dracophyllum minimum
FAMILY Epacridaceae
A dense, low plant which rises a few inches above ground level. Leaves are small, pointed, densely crowded; the closely packed, branching stems all terminate at an equal level to make a very hard mat-like surface. Small white tubular flowers form at stem tips, appearing embedded in the shrub surface. Occurs in Tas mountains above 2,500 ft, usually on alpine moorlands or scree slopes. Flowering time is Jan. to Mar.

Snow Daisy or **Silver Daisy**   *Celmisia longifoli*
FAMILY Compositae
Rising from a clump of long narrow leaves, which are green above and silver-hairy below, the tall stems (covered in fine white hairs) carry solitary terminal flower heads up to 2 in. diameter. Their centre consists of yellow disc-florets, surrounded by a ring of ray-florets whose long white ligules form the conspicuous 'petals' of each flower head. Occurs in mountain areas of south-east Aust. and Tas. Flowering time is Dec. to Feb.

Common Buttercup *Ranunculus lappaceus*
FAMILY Ranunculaceae
This low perennial may be recognised by its
branched, softly hairy flower stems, much-
divided leaves, and the long coiled beaks to the
fruits. A widespread species, from coastal to
near-alpine regions of Vic, NSW, Tas; also
occurs in SA, WA, and Qld. Seed germinates
readily. Flowering time is Sept. to Jan.

Grass Triggerplant   *Stylidium graminifolium*
FAMILY Stylidiaceae
Growing at 4,000 ft on the exposed slopes of
Cradle Mountain, Tasmania, these triggerplants
have shorter flower spikes than does the same
species in forest at lower altitudes. The basal,
tufted grass-like leaves are characteristic of this
species, which may be found throughout
temperate south-eastern Aust. and Tas, in
habitats ranging from alpine to coastal.
Flowering time is Dec. to Feb.

Alpine Groundsel   *Senecio pectinatus*
FAMILY Compositae
Found in alpine areas of NSW, Vic and Tas,
this perennial herb has spathulate to oblong,
pinnately but shallowly divided or indented
leaves. A single flower head, broadly campanulate
1 to 2 in. diameter, varying yellow to deep
orange, is carried on each stem. A cylindrical
involucre of soft bracts forms the underpart of
the flower head. Seed germinates readily, or
propagation can be from cuttings. Flowering
time is Jan. to Feb.

Snow Buttercup *Ranunculus anemoneus*
FAMILY Ranunculaceae
A plant of the alpine feldmark, the delicate-
seeming Snow Buttercup blooms as the snows
recede, its deeply lobed green leaves appearing
where the ground is still sheathed with ice. The
feldmark is an open community of alpine plants,
particularly mosses and lichens, on bare, stony
ground subject to the most severe alpine
conditions. Flowering time is Nov. to Jan.

An Alpine Boronia *Boronia rhomboidea* ▶
FAMILY Rutaceae
Near the shores of Lake Dove in the central
highlands of Tasmania, this boronia flowers
profusely in Feb.; as with most alpine wildflowers, the cold of high altitude delays its
flowering until summer. The small leaves are
rounded-rhomboid or broadly spathulate in
shape. Flowering time is Jan. to Mar.

Crasspedia glauca
FAMILY Compositae
Large composite globular flower heads are each carried at the tip of a tall slender unbranched stem, up which are scattered a few small, minutely hairy leaves. The flower head consists of numerous tiny tubular florets, each surrounded by the bracts. The interspaces are tightly packed with thin papery white bracts. Occurs in alpine areas of south-eastern Aust. Flowering time is Dec. to Feb.

Brachycome scapiformis
FAMILY Compositae
An alpine 'daisy' belonging to a genus of 52 Australian species, all small annual or perennial herbs. This plant's single terminal flower head consists of a central cluster of bisexual yellow disc-florets, surrounded by a ring of ray-florets that have outward-radiating ligules ('petals') which surround the entire head. Below are two rows of soft herbaceous involucral bracts. Flowering time is Nov. to Feb.

An Alpine Buttercup *Ranunculus gunnianus*
FAMILY Ranunculaceae
On waterlogged fenlands below Kosciusko *Ranunculus* flowers spread their glossy petals. Fully opened the flowers measure up to 1 in. diameter, borne 2 or 3 in. above ground, a single terminal flower on each stem. Flowers have 5 petals, 5 darker sepals and numerous stamens; fruits are (as with other *Ranunculus* species) hooked achenes, hanging in clusters until ripe. Seed germinates easily. Flowering time is summer—Dec. to Jan., as snow recedes.

Tasmanian Christmas Bell *Blandfordia punicea*
FAMILY Liliaceae
Growing at about 4,000 ft altitude in Cradle Mtn—Lake St Clair National Park (Tas.), these bells were flowering in Feb, months later than the mainland bell species. Flowers are borne in a terminal raceme on a tall flower stalk which each year shoots up from a thick underground rootstock. It favours swampy places where water seeps from a mountain or hill slope, or along river banks, and is confined to western Tas. Flowering time is Oct. to Mar.

Mountain Buttercup *Ranunculus muelleri*
FAMILY Ranunculaceae
From a rosette of ovate, densely hirsute leaves rise numerous flower stems each 3 to 4 in. tall; the waxy golden flowers may be more than 1 in. diameter with 5 petals, 5 sepals and numerous stamens. Leaves are only slightly lobed, usually with no more than several shallow notches towards the outer end. It grows near semi-permanent snowdrifts (flowering as they recede in summer, Nov. to Feb.) of south-eastern alpine regions.

Orange Everlasting *Helichrysum acuminatum*
FAMILY Compositae
Photographed on Tasmania's alpine plateau, but also common in alpine areas of Vic, NSW and ACT, this perennial herb has unbranched leafy flower stems 4 to 10 in. high. Each carries a single large golden to orange head up to 2 in. diameter. The many stiff papery bracts are lanceolate-acuminate in shape. Flowering time is Jan. to Mar.

Alpine Oxylobium *Oxylobium alpestre* ▶
FAMILY Papilionaceae
One of Australia's 25 species of *Oxylobium*, and probably the most showy of those found in the south-east. The orange flowers are in short terminal clusters, which often measure several inches across. The slender-elliptical to oblong leaves are net-veined, 1 to 1½ in. long, usually in groups of 3 up the stem. Occurs in alpine heaths and in mountain forests of Vic and south-east NSW. Flowering time is Nov. to Ja

This region of the continent, broadly speaking, covers the eastern half of New South Wales, southern and eastern Victoria, and part of the south-eastern corner of Queensland. Included in this region are many areas, some large, but most small and relative to the whole area, in which different environmental factors operate to produce a flora different from a strictly temperate type. The most widespread of these exclusions from this section is that which is well developed in the higher elevations (above 1,600 metres) of south-eastern New South Wales and north-eastern Victoria—the alpine heaths and herbfields. The other more different, but now not extensive, vegetation type excluded is the sub-tropical rainforest. This type of community once covered much larger areas of coastal New South Wales and south-eastern Queensland. A very large proportion of this unique vegetation was cleared, partly for valuable timber species which it contained, and partly for agricultural purposes. The few remaining areas of 'brush' or 'scrub' exist almost solely in isolated patches of varying size in State Forests, National Parks and relatively inaccessible areas of Crown Lands.

Before the advent of the white man, the greater part of the eastern temperate area was covered with many different types of plant community but today only remnants remain in most areas. Unfortunately some communities have disappeared completely or have been very considerably altered by the actions of the settlers.

East of, and along, the Great Dividing Range from Victoria to Queensland great tracts of sclerophyllous forest and woodland contain hundreds of species of plants adapted to the many combinations of environmental factors which prevail. These regions are not, however, as visually spectacular from a floristic viewpoint as the coastal sand heaths and sandstone heaths and scrubs. These latter communities occur sporadically along the east coast of the continent and are extremely rich in plant species. As the terms 'heath' and 'scrub' imply, trees are lacking from these areas, hence the prolific diversity of flower colour, size and form is seen to better advantage in the spring, the usual flowering period.

The richest flora (in term of species number) occurs on the 'poor' sandy soils of the Hawkesbury and Narrabeen sandstones of the Sydney Basin. Similar species occur on the sandy soils derived from the Permian sandstones and conglomerates of the Shoalhaven area south of Sydney, and north of Sydney near Newcastle. A very similar flora occurs on the recently deposited (in geological terms) coastal sands of the north and south coast of New South Wales, southern Queensland and south-eastern Victoria. These sandy soils, of low pH, poor in

PART 2
THE EAST

QLD.

N.S.W.

25

nutrients and with low water retention (except where topography allows swampy situations to develop) support a flora which is composed of many unrelated species, the majority of which exhibit sclerophyllous and xeromorphic characteristics. Rainfall is relatively high, 100–200 centimetres per annum, but the amount available to the plants is often much lower because of local topography and physical characteristics of the soil. A remarkably similar flora occurs on soils derived from some types of granite and similar igneous rocks in many areas of temperate eastern Australia, particularly on the 'granite belt' of the tableland area of northern New South Wales and southern Queensland. Experimental evidence indicates that lack of soil nutrients, particularly phosphorus, is partly responsible for the xeromorphic and sclerophyllous nature of the bulk of the species of the temperate regions of this country. This predominant characteristic can be seen readily in many of the photographs in this section. Soils derived from granite are different in many features from soils derived from sandstone, but the similar physical characteristics of both appear to have determined the type of vegetation and flora which has developed on them.

The dominant visual features of the flora of the area dealt with in this eastern section are species of the genus *Eucalyptus* (family Myrtaceae). Well over one hundred and fifty species of this large genus of approximately four hundred and fifty species occur in the region. The habits of these species range from

Dusky Coral-pea *Kennedia rubicunda*
FAMILY Papilionaceae
Colour: dull red. Occurrence: Qld, NSW, Vic.
Flowering: Oct. to Dec.

A Mistletoe *Dendropthoe glabrescens*
FAMILY Loranthaceae
Colour: flower tubes green at base, orange and bright red where the tip splits open.
Occurrence: east coastal. Flowering: Oct. to Jan.

tall forest trees of greater than 50 metres in height to low, many-stemmed mallees of 1–2 metres. A greater number of species of other genera however, are shrubs varying in height from 0·2 metres to 5 metres, usually forming an undergrowth under the taller eucalypts. Many of these understorey species are wattles, genus *Acacia* (family Mimosaceae). A few wattle species grow to large tree size, but the majority of them are shrubby. The other shrubby species belong to many families, the best represented being; the Myrtaceae (e.g. *Eucalyptus, Leptospermum, Melaleuca, Darwinia, Kunzea, Callistemon,* etc.); the Proteaceae (e.g. *Banksia, Grevillea, Hakea, Persoonia, Telopea, Lambertia,* etc.); the Epacridaceae (e.g. *Epacris, Leucopogon, Styphelia,* etc.) and the Papilionaceae (e.g. *Dillwynia, Pultenaea, Gompholobium, Hardenbergia, Kennedia,* etc.); plus a few species of many other genera from many families.

A large number of the genera represented in the region are endemic to Australia, indicating adaptation *in situ* to the changing environmental factors of the millions of years since plant 'invaders' from other countries arrived. Some of the genera mentioned previously contain species which occur in moister and more tropical areas of Australia, New Guinea and Indo-Malaysia, and from many aspects can be considered more 'primitive' than their more highly evolved relatives. The flora of temperate Australia is thought to have originated from several sources. The spread of species from the tropical north has probably occurred more than once. The rainforests and wet sclerophyll forests of northern and eastern coastal Australia are rich in species of many genera and many families, but there is little in common between these rainforest genera and the rest of the Australian flora. The affinities lie between the rainforest genera of Australia and Asia more than between the Australian rainforest and non-rainforest genera.

Many of the eastern temperate genera of Australia also occur in New Zealand. However, there are as many Australian genera not represented in New Zealand and vice versa, indicating some connection between the two countries at some time in the past, but also indicating a long period of separation with invasions of species of other genera from different sources to both countries. The floral dissimilarities between the two countries is as important to phytogeographers as the similarities.

The relationships between the floras of the eastern and western temperate regions of the continent are more obvious than those of any intercontinental floras. Many of the genera in most families are common to east and west, qualified however by greater speciation on one side or the other in the case of many of these genera. For example, the genus *Lambertia*

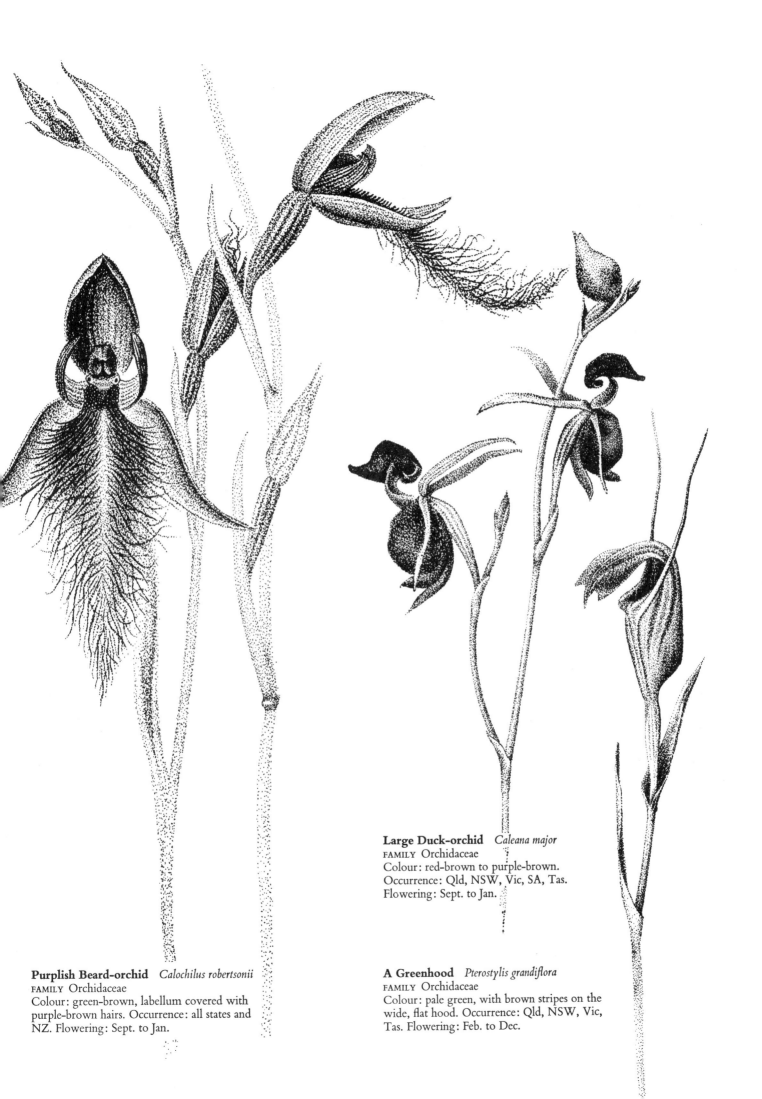

Purplish Beard-orchid *Calochilus robertsonii*
FAMILY Orchidaceae
Colour: green-brown, labellum covered with
purple-brown hairs. Occurrence: all states and
NZ. Flowering: Sept. to Jan.

Large Duck-orchid *Caleana major*
FAMILY Orchidaceae
Colour: red-brown to purple-brown.
Occurrence: Qld, NSW, Vic, SA, Tas.
Flowering: Sept. to Jan.

A Greenhood *Pterostylis grandiflora*
FAMILY Orchidaceae
Colour: pale green, with brown stripes on the
wide, flat hood. Occurrence: Qld, NSW, Vic,
Tas. Flowering: Feb. to Dec.

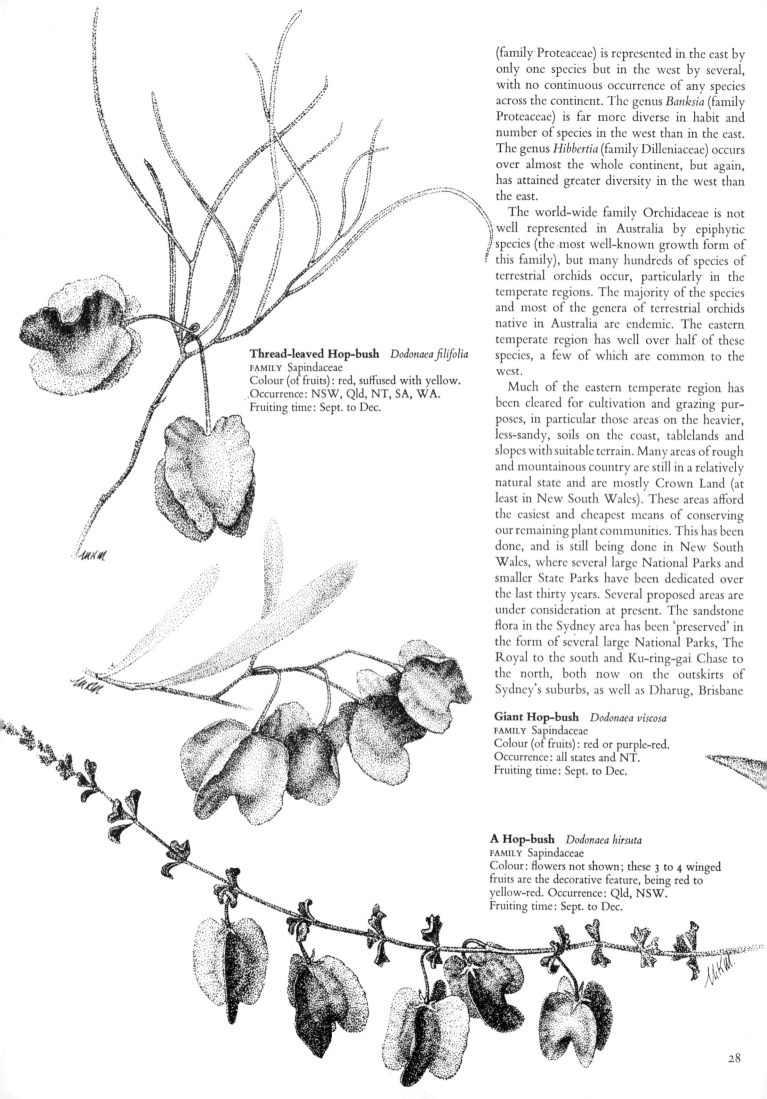

Thread-leaved Hop-bush *Dodonaea filifolia*
FAMILY Sapindaceae
Colour (of fruits): red, suffused with yellow.
Occurrence: NSW, Qld, NT, SA, WA.
Fruiting time: Sept. to Dec.

Giant Hop-bush *Dodonaea viscosa*
FAMILY Sapindaceae
Colour (of fruits): red or purple-red.
Occurrence: all states and NT.
Fruiting time: Sept. to Dec.

A Hop-bush *Dodonaea hirsuta*
FAMILY Sapindaceae
Colour: flowers not shown; these 3 to 4 winged
fruits are the decorative feature, being red to
yellow-red. Occurrence: Qld, NSW.
Fruiting time: Sept. to Dec.

(family Proteaceae) is represented in the east by only one species but in the west by several, with no continuous occurrence of any species across the continent. The genus *Banksia* (family Proteaceae) is far more diverse in habit and number of species in the west than in the east. The genus *Hibbertia* (family Dilleniaceae) occurs over almost the whole continent, but again, has attained greater diversity in the west than the east.

The world-wide family Orchidaceae is not well represented in Australia by epiphytic species (the most well-known growth form of this family), but many hundreds of species of terrestrial orchids occur, particularly in the temperate regions. The majority of the species and most of the genera of terrestrial orchids native in Australia are endemic. The eastern temperate region has well over half of these species, a few of which are common to the west.

Much of the eastern temperate region has been cleared for cultivation and grazing purposes, in particular those areas on the heavier, less-sandy, soils on the coast, tablelands and slopes with suitable terrain. Many areas of rough and mountainous country are still in a relatively natural state and are mostly Crown Land (at least in New South Wales). These areas afford the easiest and cheapest means of conserving our remaining plant communities. This has been done, and is still being done in New South Wales, where several large National Parks and smaller State Parks have been dedicated over the last thirty years. Several proposed areas are under consideration at present. The sandstone flora in the Sydney area has been 'preserved' in the form of several large National Parks, The Royal to the south and Ku-ring-gai Chase to the north, both now on the outskirts of Sydney's suburbs, as well as Dharug, Brisbane

28

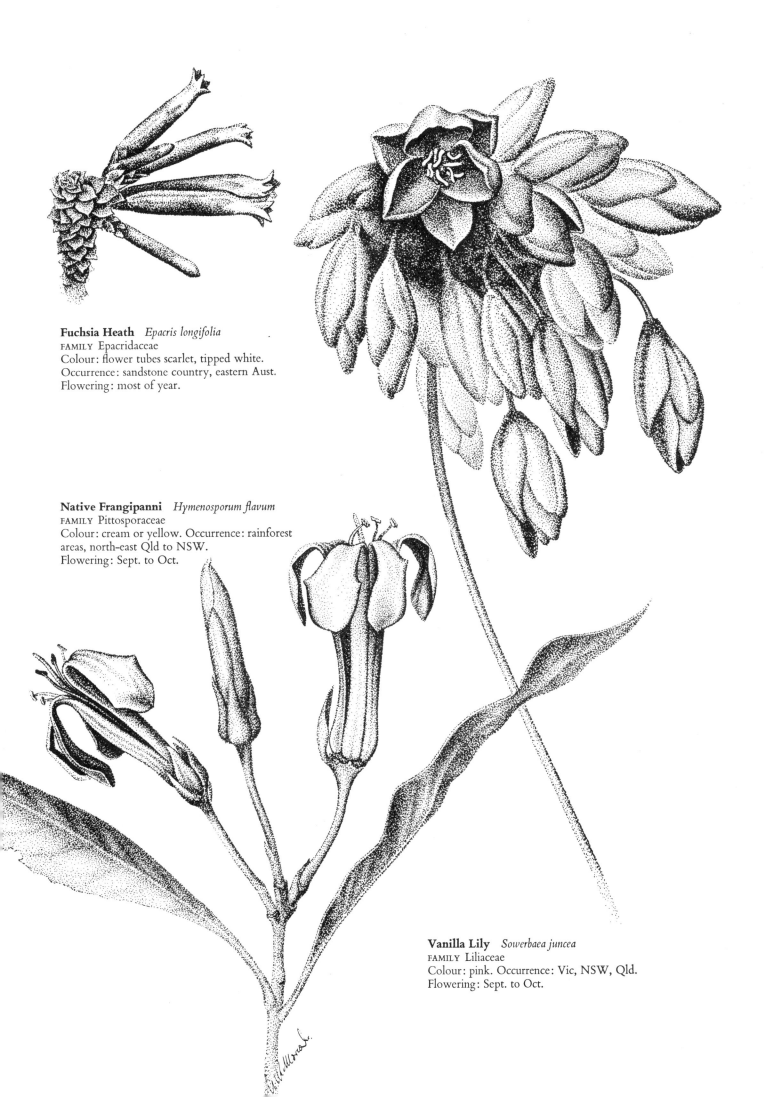

Fuchsia Heath *Epacris longifolia*
FAMILY Epacridaceae
Colour: flower tubes scarlet, tipped white.
Occurrence: sandstone country, eastern Aust.
Flowering: most of year.

Native Frangipanni *Hymenosporum flavum*
FAMILY Pittosporaceae
Colour: cream or yellow. Occurrence: rainforest
areas, north-east Qld to NSW.
Flowering: Sept. to Oct.

Vanilla Lily *Sowerbaea juncea*
FAMILY Liliaceae
Colour: pink. Occurrence: Vic, NSW, Qld.
Flowering: Sept. to Oct.

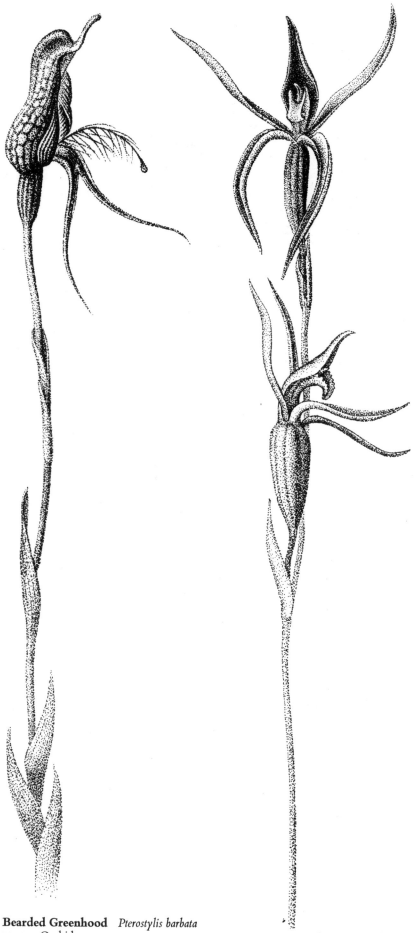

Water, Bouddi and Blue Mountains. The unsuitable nature of the shallow sandy soil for agriculture and the difficulty of home building on the rocky and deeply dissected sandstone areas resulted in their preservation late last century. One of the areas which is in urgent need of conserving is the coastal sand heath and associated plant communities of northern New South Wales and southern Queensland. Conservation proposals are current for a few small areas in New South Wales, but the clearing of all vegetation prior to mining for rutile-zircon and by tourist resort development will result in the complete loss to science and future generations of the majority of different plant communities on the north coast of New South Wales and southern Queensland.

Apart from their destruction by the direct depredations of man in the name of 'progress' and 'development', the greatest danger to these communities is fire. The Australian flora in general has evolved with fire as one of the environmental factors always present. However, the incidence and severity of fires apparently has increased since the white man. Very little is known of the effects of fire on plant communities from a long term ecological point of view in this country, hence the need for both protection of our remaining natural areas of vegetation from fire and much more research on the effects, long and short term, of fire on those communities.

Don F. Blaxell,
Botanist,
National Herbarium,
Royal Botanic Gardens,
Sydney, N.S.W.

Bearded Greenhood *Pterostylis barbata*
FAMILY Orchidaceae
Colour: bright green, with white translucent panels and fine yellow labellum (beard).
Occurrence: all states and NZ. Flowering: Sept. to Oct.

Brown Beaks *Lyperanthus suaveolens*
FAMILY Orchidaceae
Colour: sepals and petals dark brown, labellum yellow and red-brown. Occurrence: NSW, Vic, SA, Tas. Flowering: Aug. to Oct.

Don F. Blaxell, B.Sc., Dip. Agric. (Dookie), is a Botanist at the National Herbarium, Royal Botanic Gardens in Sydney. He is a Science graduate of the University of New South Wales and holds a Diploma of Agriculture from Dookie Agricultural College, Victoria. Whilst at Dookie he became interested in native plants and collected plants for, and corresponded with, Mr J. H. Willis of the National Herbarium, Melbourne.

He returned to Sydney in 1957, where he was employed as a Laboratory Assistant in the Botany Department of the University of New South Wales. He undertook a part-time course in Science, majoring in Botany and Zoology. Upon graduation he was employed as a Professional Officer in the First Year Teaching Unit, School of Biological Sciences, University of New South Wales.

In 1968, he was appointed to the staff of the New South Wales National Herbarium and is currently engaged in revisionary work on the family Orchidaceae for the Flora of New South Wales, as well as undertaking extensive field work associated with research on the genus Eucalyptus and the family Caesalpiniaceae. He has taken a great interest in matters of conservation and preservation of plant communities in general, and native orchid species in particular.

A Beard Orchid *Calochilus paludosa*
FAMILY Orchidaceae
Colour: green-brown, with petals conspicuously veined. Occurrence: Qld, NSW, Vic, SA, Tas. Flowering: Sept. to Nov.

Milkmaids *Burchardia umbellata*
FAMILY Liliaceae
Colour: white, with red centre.
Occurrence: NSW, Vic, SA, Tas, WA.
Flowering: Sept. to Nov.

NATIONAL PARKS AND WILDFLOWER RESERVES

BLUE MOUNTAINS NATIONAL PARK (NSW)
40 m. W of Sydney, off Great Western Highway.

Distinctive wildflowers on sandstone plateau heights; dry sclerophyll forest with wet sclerophyll in gorges. Best flowers seen in spring.

BRISBANE WATERS NATIONAL PARK (NSW)
40 m. N of Sydney, near Gosford.

Displays of Waratah, Christmas Bells in November. Rough sandstone with dry sclerophyll forest, patches of sub-tropical rainforest. July to Dec.

BUNYA MOUNTAINS NATIONAL PARK (QLD)
60 m. NW from Toowoomba.

Rainforest epiphytic orchids, ferns, huge Bunya Pines. Rainforests and open hardwood forests.

CARNARVON NATIONAL PARK (QLD)
On Great Divide about 60 m. NW of Injune, 250 m. W of Bundaberg.

Sandstone country, many wildflowers in early spring; ferns, palms in rugged gorges. Winter and spring months.

CUNNINGHAM'S GAP NATIONAL PARK (QLD)
70 m. SW from Brisbane via Cunningham Highway.

On Great Dividing Range, peaks to 4,100 ft with dense rainforest, open forest, epiphytic orchids, palm groves, ferns.

DHARUG NATIONAL PARK (NSW)
On N side of Hawkesbury R. near Wiseman's Ferry, 46 m. N of Sydney.

Rugged sandstone plateau with dry sclerophyll forest, many Sydney-sandstone wildflowers in spring months.

DORRIGO STATE PARK (NSW)
On hwy 2 m. E of Dorrigo, 360 m. N of Sydney.

Mountain slopes with sub-tropical rainforest and dry sclerophyll forest. Giant trees, epiphytic orchids, ferns, palms, vines, flame trees. Spring and autumn.

GIBRALTAR RANGE NATIONAL PARK (NSW)
Midway between Glen Innes and Grafton on Gwydir Hwy, 450 m. N of Sydney.

Large Christmas Bells on swamps Nov.–Dec., Waratahs Oct.–Nov. Rainforest on mountain slopes to 3,000 ft, with flame trees Oct.–Nov., many epiphytic orchids, ground orchids, glory peas.

GIRRAWEEN NATIONAL PARK (QLD)
Near Wyberba, E of Cunningham Hwy just N of NSW border.

Rugged granite peaks to 4,156 ft; great variety of 'granite belt' wildflowers Sept. to Nov.

KANANGRA-BOYD NATIONAL PARK (NSW)
Blue Mtns W of Sydney, 15 m. from Jenolan Caves.

Rugged high sandstone plateau with great variety of wildflowers. Wet sclerophyll forest (big gums, ferns) on lower slopes, gorges.

KU-RING-GAI CHASE NATIONAL PARK (NSW)
15 m. N of Sydney between Pacific Hwy and Pittwater.

A profusion of wildflowers in spring, Christmas Bells. Dry sclerophyll forest with patches of rainforest.

LAMINGTON NATIONAL PARK (QLD)
On McPherson Ranges above NSW border, inland from Gold Coast.

Magnificent rainforests with tree ferns, epiphytic orchids, ferns, many flowering trees, Antarctic Beech forest at high altitude.

MOOLOOLAH RIVER NATIONAL PARK (QLD)
60 m. N of Brisbane, 3 m. E of Bruce Hwy.

Coastal plain fronting Mooloolah R., a region very rich in wildflowers.

MORTON NATIONAL PARK (NSW)
100 m. S of Sydney on Moss Vale to Nowra road.

A dissected sandstone plateau, deep gorges. Wet and dry sclerophyll forests, sub-tropical rainforest.

MT NEBO AND MT GLORIOUS (QLD)
30 m. NW of Brisbane.

Patches of rainforest with palm groves, cabbage-tree palms, arboreal ferns, etc.

NEW ENGLAND NATIONAL PARK (NSW)
320 m. N from Sydney, 45 m. E from Armidale.

Great altitude range, from almost sea level to 5,000 ft. Vegetation from sub-tropical rainforest to sub-alpine. Red Cedars, Antarctic Beech forest, Snow Gums. Rainforest orchids, ferns; a different flora on the heights.

NOOSA NATIONAL PARK (QLD)
On coast 110 m. N from Brisbane.

Small area of rainforest with Hoop-pine, Kauri Pine, pandanus; prolific spring wildflowers on open forest coastal plains.

ROYAL NATIONAL PARK (NSW)
20 m. S of Sydney, entrance from Princes Hwy.

Extensive plateau-top heathlands above coastal cliffs rich in flowering species; sub-tropical rainforest along river gully.

TAMBORINE MOUNTAIN PARKS (QLD)
Inland from Gold Coast, between Brisbane and NSW border.

Rainforest: Piccabeen Palms, Macrozamia Grove. Rainforest orchids, ferns.

WARRUMBUNGLE NATIONAL PARK (NSW)
Northern inland NSW, 300 m. from Sydney, 20 m. W of Coonabarabran.

Dry sclerophyll forest around eroded volcanic spires. Wildflowers of both inland plains and coastal areas. Early spring.

Large-Flowered Christmas Bell

Blandfordia grandiflora

FAMILY Liliaceae
A large-flowered form of the common Christmas Bell (*B. nobilis*). The floral tubes are almost 3 in. long, and more broadly dilated, being the most bell-shaped of the 4 *Blandfordia* species. Occurs on the coast and tablelands of NSW from the Hawkesbury and Blue Mountains northwards to south-east Qld. Bells are easily grown from seed. A moist, sunny position is best. Flowering time is Nov. to Jan.

32

Common Fringe-Myrtle *Calytrix tetragona*
FAMILY Myrtaceae
The flowers of this small, heath-foliaged, aromatic shrub have long, bristle-like awns that tip each sepal of the pink to white flowers. These sepals remain after petals fall, acquiring a rich bronze colour. Occurs throughout temperate Australia, favouring sandy soils. Seed can be difficult to germinate; propagation is a little easier from new-wood cuttings. Flowering time is Sept. to Nov.

Native May *Phebalium squamulosum*
FAMILY Rutaceae
Dense clusters of tiny bright yellow flowers are borne in terminal corymbs; the lanceolate leaves are shiny, dark green above, brown-white and scaly below. Occurs between the coast and the Divide, from Vic to Qld, in sandstone and granite country. Seed germination is often difficult, cuttings are easier method of propagation. Flowering time is Sept. to Oct.

Pink Wax-Flower *Eriostemon lanceolatus*
FAMILY Rutaceae
A small erect shrub with grey-green, lanceolate leaves, and flowers which are the largest of the *Eriostemons*. The 5 waxy pink petals form a flower up to 1 in. across, borne in profusion. This *Eriostemon* is most prolific on the coastal sandstone country near Sydney. Flowering time is Sept. to Oct.

Small-Leaved Boronia *Boronia microphylla*
FAMILY Rutaceae
A low shrub with small obovate or oblong-cuneate leaves 4–6 mm long. As with other boronia, of which there are 60 to 70 endemic species scattered through all states, the foliage contains oil glands which give off a strongly aromatic perfume when crushed. Favours uppe mountain and heathland on Hawkesbury sandstone or granite. Flowering time is Oct. to Jan.

Banks Grevillea *Grevillea banksii*
FAMILY Proteaceae
A tall shrub often growing up to 15 ft. Foliage is soft grey-green, leaves deeply divided into narrow-leaflets. The red, cream or green flower racemes, 3 to 6 in. long, are carried erect at the tips of the branches, and attract nectar eating birds. This grevillea occurs on open plains of Qld often on poor soils. The red-flowered form is widely cultivated, making an attractive garden shrub. Flowering time is spring to autumn.

Silky Purple-Flag or **Bush Iris**
Patersonia sericea
FAMILY Iridaceae
The stems, leaves, bracts of this species are silky-woolly. A genus of about 20 species, perennial herbs with tough, grass-like leaves and underground rhizomes. The flowers appear, a few at a time, from a terminal cluster sheathed within bracts. They are extremely delicate, lasting only a few hours. Occurs along east coast from Vic to Qld. Flowering time is Sept. to Nov.

Match Heads *Comesperma ericinum* ▶
FAMILY Polygalaceae
A slender-stemmed, erect small shrub carrying many pointed terminal panicles of lilac-pink flowers. Each little flower in bud resembles a matchhead, when open a pea flower, but with sepals forming the wide wings, and petals making the central keel over the 8 stamens. Occurs in Qld, NSW and Vic, commonly in granite country. Flowering time is Sept. to De

Long-Leaved Smokebush
Conospermum longifolium
FAMILY Proteaceae
A forest undershrub which carries a mass of tiny
white flowers, arranged in dense terminal
corymbs, at the tips of slender branchlets of
equal height. Leaves are slender-lanceolate,
6 to 9 in. long. Occurs in dry sclerophyll forest,
eastern NSW. Propagation from cutting easiest,
though slow. Flowering time is Sept. to Nov.

Waratah *Telopea speciossima* ▶
FAMILY Proteaceae
A tall upright, multi-stemmed shrub, with thick
stiff, tooth-edged leaves. Individual flowers are
similar to those of Grevilleas, but arranged in a
very large terminal head, surrounded at the base
by an involucre of crimson bracts. Occurs on
rock and sandy soils from the Blue Mountains
and Hunter River northwards almost to Qld
border. Flowering time is Sept. to Nov.

Christmas Bell *Blandfordia nobilis*
FAMILY Liliaceae
Best-known of the 4 *Blandfordia* species, this bell occurs profusely on damp areas of sandstone country around Sydney, particularly in Ku-ring-gai Chase. Its flowers are clustered in terminal racemes on long stalks rising from stiff, sharp, grass-like leaves. Six perianth segments unite to form the bell-like tube, which broadens suddenly at the base (stem end).
Flowering time is Nov. to Dec.

Flannel Flower *Actinotus helianthi*
FAMILY Umbelliferae
A smallish herb (usually biennial) with grey, felted, divided leaves and creamy-white flowers carried on tall slender stem. The daisy-like flowers, 2–3 in. across are (like the rest of the plant) covered in soft silky down. It grows in sandy or rocky areas of coastal NSW and Qld, and in some places inland, such as Warrumbungle National Park. Seeds germinate readily, mass-planted in a well-drained position. Flowering time is Sept. to Feb.

Common Everlastings *Helichrysum apiculatum*
FAMILY Compositae
Many small golden flower heads are clustered into large terminal corymbs; leaves, which may be wide or narrow, and stems are covered in fine white hairs giving a greyish appearance. This is a variable species, occurring in all states and the NT. It is easily grown from seed. Flowering time is Oct. to Dec.

Slipper Orchid *Cryptostylis subulata*
FAMILY Orchidaceae
A small herbaceous terrestrial orchid with long, upright, broad petiolate leaves. Each plant bears several greenish-yellow flowers, with a distinctive large red-brown veined labellum. This orchid mimics the attractions of the female ichneumon wasp, attracting the males which serve as its pollen carriers. Occurs in semi-shaded positions beneath forest undergrowth from Vic to Qld, and in SA and Tas. Flowering time is Nov. to April.

Guinea Flower *Hibbertia obtusifolia*
FAMILY Dilleniaceae
Though the majority of *Hibbertia*'s belong to WA, the genus has representatives throughout Australia except in arid regions. The flowers of this species are large, solitary, terminal, with 5 sepals, 5 soft spreading petals and numerous stamens. It is a small, almost procumbent shrub, of the open dry sclerophyll forest. Propagation is easiest by cuttings, and a well-drained site is required. Flowering time is Aug. to Dec.

Fuchsia Heath *Epacris longifolia*
FAMILY Epacridaceae
A low straggling shrub with slender wiry stems and rigid, sharp-pointed triangular leaves. The long corolla-tubes (12–20 mm) are red, tipped with white, and hang from the leaf axils in one-sided fashion along the branches. Occurs in heathlands and dry sclerophyll forest, particularly on sandstone, along NSW coast and Dividing Range. Flowers most of the year.

Wallum Bottlebrush *Callistemon pachyphyllus*
FAMILY Myrtaceae
Callistemons, of which there are 20 species, carry their flowers in close-packed cylindrical spikes. Leaves are tough, stiff, alternate in arrangement up the stems. This species is red-flowered in some districts, yellow-green elsewhere. Occurs on swampy or sandy soils of coastal NSW and south-east Qld. Flowering time is Oct. to Dec.

Cassia odorata
FAMILY Caesalpiniaceae
Cassias, forming a genus within the pea family, have pinnately divided leaves. The flowers, which may be open or cup-shaped depending on species, have up to 10 stamens, and the fruit is a thin pea-type pod.

River Rose *Bauera rubioides*
FAMILY Baueraceae
A small wiry shrub with a distinctive leaf arrangement. The leaves are each divided into 3 small leaflets, and by their opposite placement appear as a whorl right round the stem. Flower colour varies from rich pink to white. Abundant in moist coastal forests, along creeks and swampy heaths, from SA to Qld, and in Tas. Flowering time is Oct. to Nov.

Drumsticks *Isopogon anemonifolius*
FAMILY Proteaceae
An erect shrub with stiff, much-divided leaves. The thin golden perianth tubes push outwards from a hard central cone, beginning from the base, then dying from the base upwards until finally only a greyish woolly globular cone remains. This is a plant of sandstone, granite and sandy country of the east coast and Dividing Range, extending northwards into southern Qld. Flowering time is spring and summer.

Honeyflower or **Mountain Devil**
Lambertia formosa
FAMILY Proteaceae
The genus *Lambertia* contains 10 species, all confined to WA except *formosa*, which occurs in sandstone regions of NSW. The deep tubular flowers, in clusters at the end of branches and surrounded by bracts, are filled with nectar which attracts its bird pollinators. The fruit is a sharp-beaked, horned woody capsule, hence the name 'mountain devil'. Flowering any time of year, best Sept. to Dec.

Sungold or **Golden Paper Daisy** ▶
          Helichrysum bracteatum, var. *viscosum*
FAMILY Compositae
Australia has over 100 species of *Helichrysum*, annuals or perennials with papery flower heads made up of rows of shiny stiff bracts. *Helichrysum bracteatum* is widely distributed through all states. It is a variable species, with soft aromatic leaves and flower heads up to 2 in. across. Shown growing in Warrumbungle National Park are plants of the variety *viscosum*. Flowering time is Oct. to Dec.

Dianella species
FAMILY Liliaceae
A genus of 5 Australian species, consisting of herbs with long strap-like sheathing leaves, at the base, or around the upper stem also. Flowers are star-like, arranged in panicles, with 6 perianth segments and 6 stamens. Fruit is a shiny blue berry containing several seeds. Flowering time is Oct. to Dec.

A Yellow Everlasting ▶
Helichrysum obcordatum, subspecies *major*
FAMILY Compositae
From a walk track in the Warrumbungle National Park, NSW there spreads a panorami view over the volcanic spires of the Warrumbungle Range. Here, on narrow rock ledges, grows this pale yellow *Helichrysum*, wit each tall stem bearing a wide head of small, close-packed papery flowers. Flowering time is Oct. to Dec.

Drumsticks *Isopogon anemonifolius*
FAMILY Proteaceae
An erect shrub with stiff, much-divided leaves. The thin golden perianth tubes push outwards from a hard central cone, beginning from the base, then dying from the base upwards until finally only a greyish woolly globular cone remains. This is a plant of sandstone, granite and sandy country of the east coast and Dividing Range, extending northwards into southern Qld. Flowering time is spring and summer.

Christmas Bell *Blandfordia nobilis*
FAMILY Liliaceae
Best-known of the 4 *Blandfordia* species, this bell occurs profusely on damp areas of sandstone country around Sydney, particularly in Ku-ring-gai Chase. Its flowers are clustered in terminal racemes on long stalks rising from stiff, sharp, grass-like leaves. Six perianth segments unite to form the bell-like tube, which broadens suddenly at the base (stem end).
Flowering time is Nov. to Dec.

Showy Podolepis *Podolepis jaceoides*
FAMILY Compositae
A tall herbaceous annual, with solitary termina flower heads up to 2 in. diameter. Leaves are long, lanceolate, soft, green. Flower heads are hemispherical, with numerous papery involucr bracts making up the undersurface.
Occurs in varied situations from sea level to sub-alpine, Vic and Tas; also in NSW, Qld. Flowering time is Sept. to Feb.

Over **Heath-Leaved Banksia** *Banksia ericifolia*
FAMILY Proteaceae
High above the cliffs of the NSW coast in Royal National Park, grow low stunted shrubs of the Heath-leaved Banksia; back from the windswept cliff edge the species attains the

stature of a small tree. It has attractive foliage fine, close-packed half-inch leaves, and foot-lor orange-gold flowers, which open out from the top of the spike downwards. Occurs east coast sandstone country northwards to Qld.
Flowering time is spring, summer, autumn.

Gymea Lily or **Giant Lily** *Doryanthes excelsa*
FAMILY Agavaceae
From a clump of 6-ft, sword-like leaves arises a
leafy scape or flowering stem 15 ft or more tall,
bearing a 12-in. wide head of large, trumpet-
shaped pink flowers. The abundant nectar
attracts many birds. Common around Sydney
on sandstone coastal ranges, it is distributed
northwards into Qld. Although seed germinates
easily growth is slow. A deep, well-drained
soil is needed. Flowering time is Oct. to Nov.

Golden Glory Pea or **Broad-Leaved Glory
Pea** *Gompholobium latifolium*
FAMILY Papilionaceae
The large, deep yellow to delicate light yellow
pea flowers are carried in profusion along
slender supply stems among soft narrow-
lanceolate leaves. Individual flowers are borne
in the leaf-axils, and may measure up to 1½ in.
across the standard. Occurs along the east coast
and nearby mountains from Vic to Qld, in dry
sclerophyll forest on sandstone or granite.
Flowering time is Oct. to Nov.

Purplish Beard-Orchid *Calochilus robertsonii*
FAMILY Orchidaceae
A long, bearded labellum is the distinctive
feature of this orchid and the 7 or 8 other
species of *Calochilus*. This species has a narrow,
deeply channelled leaf, an eye-like gland at
either side of the base of the column, and
metallic-purple hairs (the beard) on the labellum.
Occurs in all states. Flowering time is Sept. to
Dec.

Match Heads *Comesperma ericinum* ◀
FAMILY Polygalaceae
A slender-stemmed, erect small shrub carrying
many pointed terminal panicles of lilac-pink
flowers. Each little flower in bud resembles a
matchhead, when open a pea flower, but with
sepals forming the wide wings, and petals
making the central keel over the 8 stamens.
Occurs in Qld, NSW and Vic, commonly in
granite country. Flowering time is Sept. to Dec.

Small-Leaved Boronia *Boronia microphylla*
FAMILY Rutaceae
A low shrub with small obovate or oblong-
cuneate leaves 4–6 mm long. As with other
boronia, of which there are 60 to 70 endemic
species scattered through all states, the foliage
contains oil glands which give off a strongly
aromatic perfume when crushed. Favours upper
mountain and heathland on Hawkesbury
sandstone or granite. Flowering time is Oct.
to Jan.

Large-Flowered Christmas Bell ▶
A Yellow-faced Honeyeater seeks nectar at a
Christmas Bell (*Blandfordia grandiflora*) and
carries the golden pollen from plant to plant.

Coast Banksia or **White Honeysuckle** *Ove*
FAMILY Proteaceae   *Banksia integrifolia*
Quite a large tree, with gnarled trunk and
greyed bark. The dark green leaves are linear-
lanceolate, with edges entire. In many parts of
its wide range this is a coastal tree, but in place
grows inland. Winter flowering.

This vast arid and semi-arid area can be harsh and forbidding, or even ruthless, to man and beast, but it can also show wondrous, unexpected beauty. The starkness of bare lands during drought is, after good rains, softened by a green film of germinating plants whose seeds have miraculously survived the enforced dessication. Subsequently, in springtime—this could be late July or during August, the land can be glowing with the colour of purple or pink vetches, *Swainsona*, yellow and pink daisies, *Senecio*, *Helipterum*, and *Helichrysum* species, red Sturt's Desert Pea, *Clianthus formosus*, and white *Blennodia*.

To fully appreciate the gift of plant life in our drier areas, it is necessary to understand some of the conditions which exist. The rainfall in this area was once more ample, but a period of aridity began about six thousand years ago, and the vegetation of today is the result of adaptation over this period.

Drought is a recurring feature. The rainfall averages from two to about fifteen inches annually, but its outstanding characteristic is its unreliability. For instance, in Alice Springs in 1918 the rainfall was 420 points, yet in 1920, the rainfall was 2,857 points. There is a tendency for more rain to fall in summer in the northern part of the arid zone, while in the southern areas, particularly the southern part of Western Australia, the rainfall has a tendency to be greater in winter.

Within these rainfall patterns, the average amount for a year may not reflect the true effective rain. For instance, dependent on latitude and altitude, about fifty points will be sufficient to initiate the growth of plants in winter, but over one hundred points are needed in summer. Then a follow-up rain would be needed within a few weeks to ensure continued growth. Rains of about double these figures will have a carry-over effect on the vegetation and could ensure a good season.

Extremes of temperature are a well-known feature of arid lands, with summer temperatures of 100°F occurring for long periods, and frosts can occur from May to September. Evaporation rates are high, humidity is usually low, and dews are rare.

As mentioned, the plants have adapted to these conditions and have evolved certain strategies to survive and grow. Perennials, including the tree species, are dormant or almost so, during winter, and the growth begins after the cessation of the main frost period. Excessive frosts can damage certain species, and this happened in central Australia near Coratippra Station in the early 1960s when trees of Whitewood, *Atalaya hemiglauca*, were badly frosted. Some annuals such as Yellow Daisy, *Senecio gregorii*, species of *Helipterum*, *Calocephalus*, *Atriplex* and many others can take

PART 3 THE CENTRE

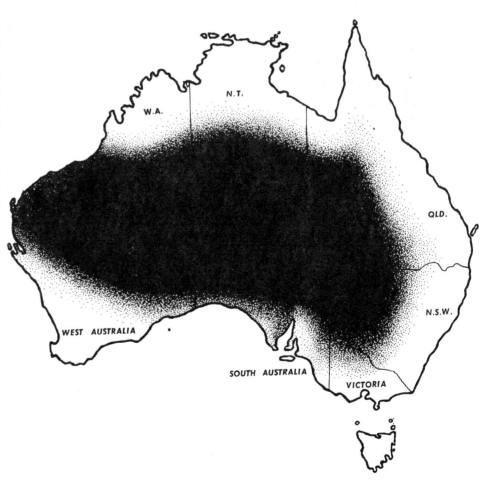

Large Green Pussytail *Ptilotus macrocephalus*
FAMILY Amaranthaceae
Colour: individual flowers are green, buried in fluffy creamy-white or greenish spikes.
Occurrence: red sand or rocky hills, central Aust. Flowering: winter to early summer.

advantage of small falls of rain, and even without follow-up rain can achieve flowering and seeding at a height of only several inches, thus ensuring survival. A small group, notably the pink-flowering Parakeelya, *Calandrinia*, and the closely related *Portulaca* resist the dry atmosphere with thick, succulent leaves. Perennial grasses such as the Mitchell grasses, *Astrebla*, evade the dry winter with dormancy. Other grasses such as the Spinifex, *Triodia* and *Plectrachne* species, are truly drought-resistant by virtue of their compact, tussock habit and sclerophyllous, needle-shaped leaves and stems.

An important aspect of arid zone vegetation is the occurrence of micro-environments where growth is more favoured. Such places are the banks and beds of seasonal streams, pockets of soil among rocks, small depressions in otherwise flat ground, the soil surrounding large rock outcrops, the shady canopy of isolated trees, and also the shelter and protection of fallen trees and shrubs. Near Alice Springs there was some evidence to suggest that the Red Kangaroo utilises one of these micro-environments, namely the depressions known as 'gilgais', in clayey plains, by grazing on the species in these areas. Extra water running off the hard clay soils into these gilgais caused more succulent growth on the plants, particularly the dominant grass, neverfail, *Eragrostis setifolia*.

The arid zone vegetation has a number of broad associations of plants. The 'desert' is the

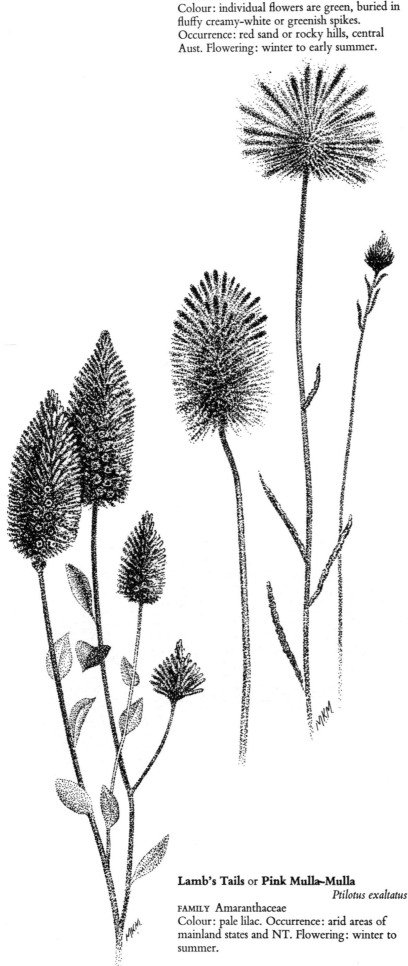

Lamb's Tails or **Pink Mulla-Mulla**
Ptilotus exaltatus
FAMILY Amaranthaceae
Colour: pale lilac. Occurrence: arid areas of mainland states and NT. Flowering: winter to summer.

Eremophila latrobei
FAMILY Myoporaceae
Colour: bright red. Occurrence: mulga plains, interior of WA. Flowering: April to Oct.

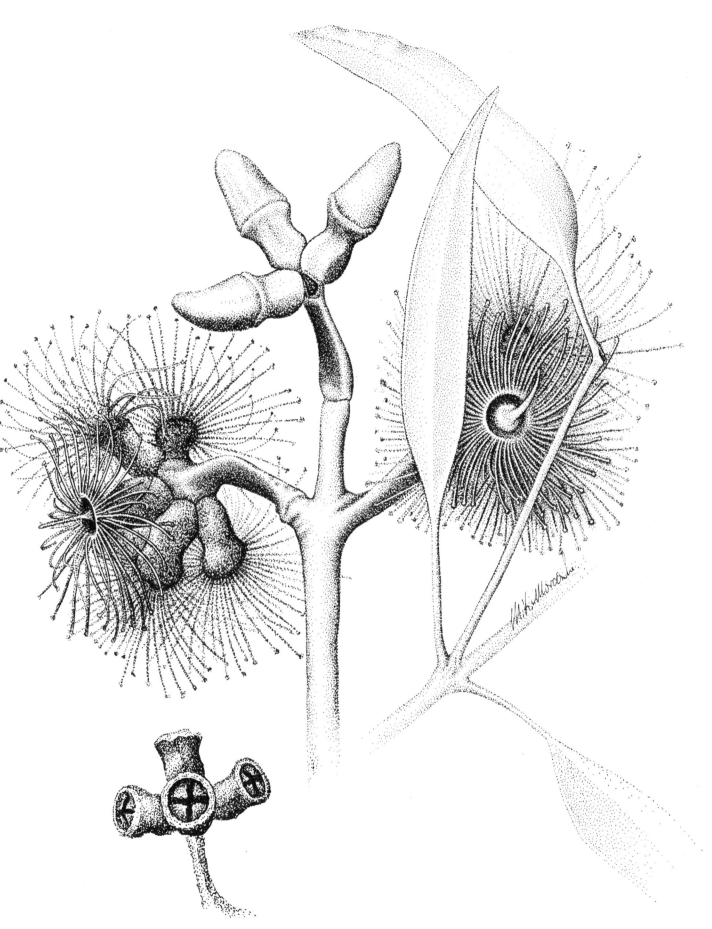

Strickland's Gum *Eucalyptus stricklandii*
FAMILY Myrtaceae
Colour: filaments yellow, buds and fruits
powdery-white surfaced. Occurrence: western
edge of Nullarbor Plain, interior of WA.
Flowering: Dec. to Jan., sometimes to Mar.

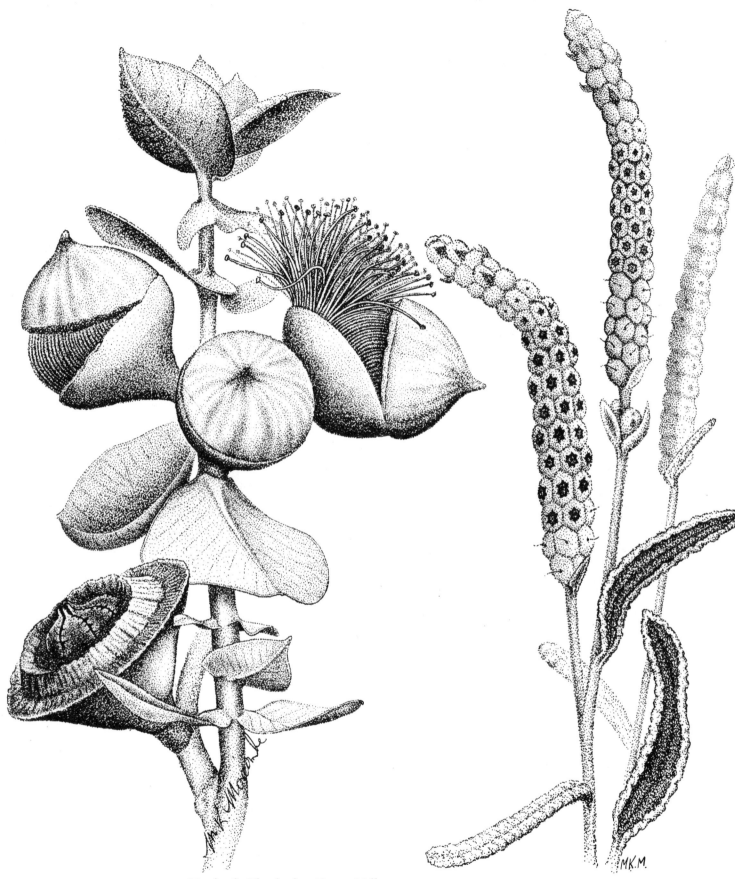

Muttlecah, Blue-bush or **Desert Mallee**
Eucalyptus macrocarpa
FAMILY Myrtaceae
Colour: filaments brilliant scarlet to pink;
foliage, buds, fruits silvery grey.
Occurrence: central west-coastal WA extending
well inland on grey sands.
Flowering: July to Jan.

Lamb's Tails *Newcastelia hexarrhena*
FAMILY Verbenaceae
Colour: small flowers of violet to mauve buried
in fluffy white spikes. Occurrence: spinifex
desert east of Kalgoorlie. Flowering: July to Oct.

large area of sand-dunes such as in the Simpson Desert, the Gibson Desert, and parts of the Victoria Desert. These areas are still not occupied by the pastoral industry, but are now being prospected by oil companies. The sand-ridges have grasses such as Spinifex, *Triodia*, and Cane Grass, *Zygochloa paradoxa*, together with some small drought-evading perennials and some drought-resistant shrubs and small trees such as Umbrella Wattle, *Acacia ligulata*. Between the sand-ridges are scattered trees and shrubs, including several species of *Acacia* and somewhat similar vegetation is found on more extensive sand-plains. Known popularly in Australia as 'scrub' are the various associations such as those of Mulga, *Acacia aneura*, Gidyea, *Acacia georginae*, Witchetty Bush, *Acacia kempeana*, Myall, *Acacia pendula*, and Prickly Wattle, *Acacia victoriae*. The riverine vegetation is a ribbon of influence perhaps varying up to about one hundred yards from the stream bed, usually with the river red gum, *Eucalyptus camaldulensis*, lining the watercourse. Here there are scattered *Acacia* species, some 'Native Fuchsias', *Eremophila*, and several *Cassia* species. In the mountain ranges there are often some different species, even some unique species such as the cycad, *Macrozamia macdonnellii*, and the unexpected palm, *Livistona mariae*, both in the Macdonnell Ranges of central Australia. Clayey soil areas where seasonal water may lie surrounded by Coolibah, *Eucalyptus microtheca*, salt-affected swamps where bindyis, *Bassia*, samphires, *Arthrocnemum* and *Pachycornia*, and saltbushes, *Atriplex*, are some other smaller, though widespread, communities. Then, there are the treeless plains, such as on the Nullarbor Plain where the vegetation is dominated by species of *Bassia*, *Atriplex* and *Kochia*. Further north, the extensive treeless Barkly Tableland is dominated by several Mitchell grasses, particularly Barley Mitchell Grass, *Astrebla pectinata*.

Eremophila mackinlayi
FAMILY Myoporaceae
Colour: deep violet. Occurrence: mulga scrub of far western deserts. Flowering: July to Sept.

Coral Gum *Eucalyptus torquata*
FAMILY Myrtaceae
Colour: filaments pink or scarlet; buds and fruits usually suffused with orange or red.
Occurrence: stony hills, red soils, Coolgardie-Norseman area, inland WA.
Flowering: Nov. to Jan.

Helipterum rubellum
FAMILY Compositae
Colour: deep magenta-red. Occurrence: widespread through southern interior of WA.
Flowering: Aug. to Sept.

53

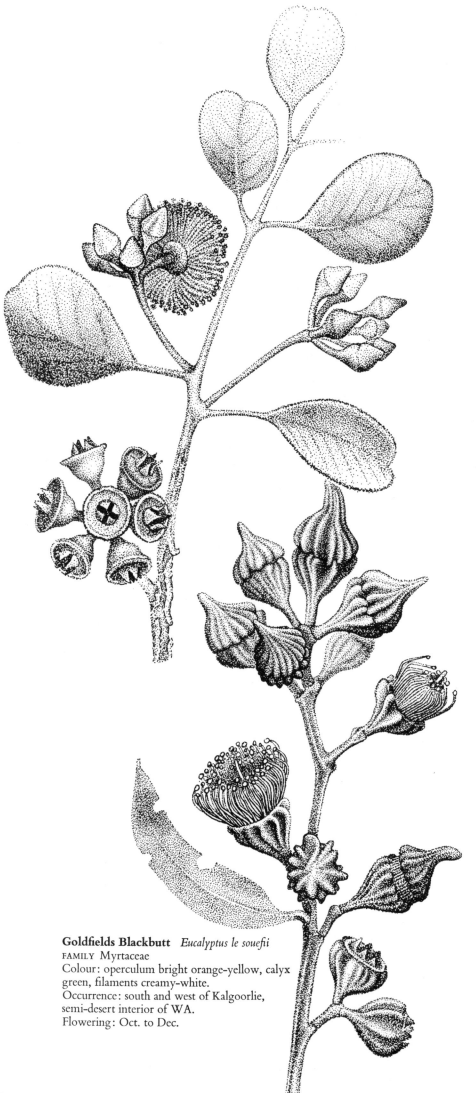

Goldfields Blackbutt *Eucalyptus le souefii*
FAMILY Myrtaceae
Colour: operculum bright orange-yellow, calyx
green, filaments creamy-white.
Occurrence: south and west of Kalgoorlie,
semi-desert interior of WA.
Flowering: Oct. to Dec.

While species of *Acacia* are most common in the drier areas of Australia, the area of Western Australia surrounding Kalgoorlie contains over one hundred species of *Eucalyptus*—about a fifth of the known number. Trees of great variety and beauty are found here, including valued ornamental species such as the yellow-flowered Strickland Gum, *Eucalyptus strick-landii*, the Lemon-flowered Gum, *Eucalyptus woodwardii*, the pink or red-flowered Gungurru, *Eucalyptus caesia*, Coral Gum, *Eucalyptus torquata*, and the sculptured-fruited Kingsmill's Mallee, *Eucalyptus kingsmillii*. The attractive salmon and bronze trunks of the Salmon Gum, *Eucalyptus salmonophloia*, and Gimlet Gum, *Eucalyptus salubris*, contrast with the blackbutts, *Eucalyptus clelandii*, and *Eucalyptus lesouefii*. From central Australia are several attractive mallees, the Blue Mallee, *Eucalyptus gamophylla*, and the Red-bud Mallee, *Eucalyptus pachyphylla*. One eucalypt seen by comparatively few people occurs in central Australia and into Western Australia; this is the Marble Gum, *Eucalyptus gongylocarpa*. A eucalypt which has become a photographer's 'must' is the Ghost Gum, *Eucalyptus papuana*, also found in this arid area.

Shrubs which are more prevalent in the arid zone include many species of *Cassia*, *Eremophila*, *Dodonaea*, *Capparis*, *Myoporum* and also the dwarf shrubs of *Frankenia*. Other trees of importance in this region are Whitewood, *Atalaya hemiglauca*, Wilga, *Geijera parviflora*, Rosewood, *Heterodendrum oleifolium*, Desert Oak, *Casuarina decaisneana*, Needlewood, *Hakea leucoptera*, Beefwood, *Grevillea striata*, Blood-wood, *Eucalyptus terminalis*, Quandong, *Santalum acuminatum*, Pittosporum, *Pittosporum phylliraeoides*, and White Cypress Pine, known widely as *Callitris glauca*, but also called *Callitris hugelii*.

Because the rainfall in this vast zone of Australia is mostly insufficient to sustain agriculture, the area has developed as a huge grazing area for sheep and cattle. There is a history of misuse of the vegetation in many areas. For instance, in the New South Wales western district in 1891, sheep numbers rose to 15,400,000, and with ensuing drought in 1901–2 these flocks dropped to 3,500,000. It is significant that the sheep population has *never* again attained the same high figure. A similar situation arose in central Australia during the years leading up to 1958 when cattle numbers reached 360,000, then dropped during droughts to 80,000 in 1965; it seems likely that the high figures will not again be realised. Historically, arid lands of the world have been ruined by droughts, grazing, and wars, and in some of these countries with large human populations there is very little natural firewood. Foresters from these countries have sought information on Australian arid zone species of shrubs which would produce firewood quickly.

The vegetation in these drier areas of Australia is in a very precarious balance with the climate and native grazing animals. Only wise management of sheep and cattle will ensure that the vegetation is not removed to the point where erosion can take place.

The growth of wildflowers in the arid zone is one of the miracles of nature. Trees which grow to sixty or more feet, the spectacular beauty of countryside red with Sturt's Desert Pea, and the mulga which covers more country than any other tree or shrub species in Australia are only a few of the special appeals of the plants of this area.

George M. Chippendale,
Taxonomic Botanist,
Forestry and Timber Bureau,
Canberra, A.C.T.

Fuchsia Gum *Eucalyptus forrestiana*
FAMILY Myrtaceae
Colour: buds, winged calyx, fruits scarlet, filaments yellow. Occurrence: interior of WA. (Salmon Gums–Grasspatch area.)
Flowering: Dec. to May; colourful buds for a longer period.

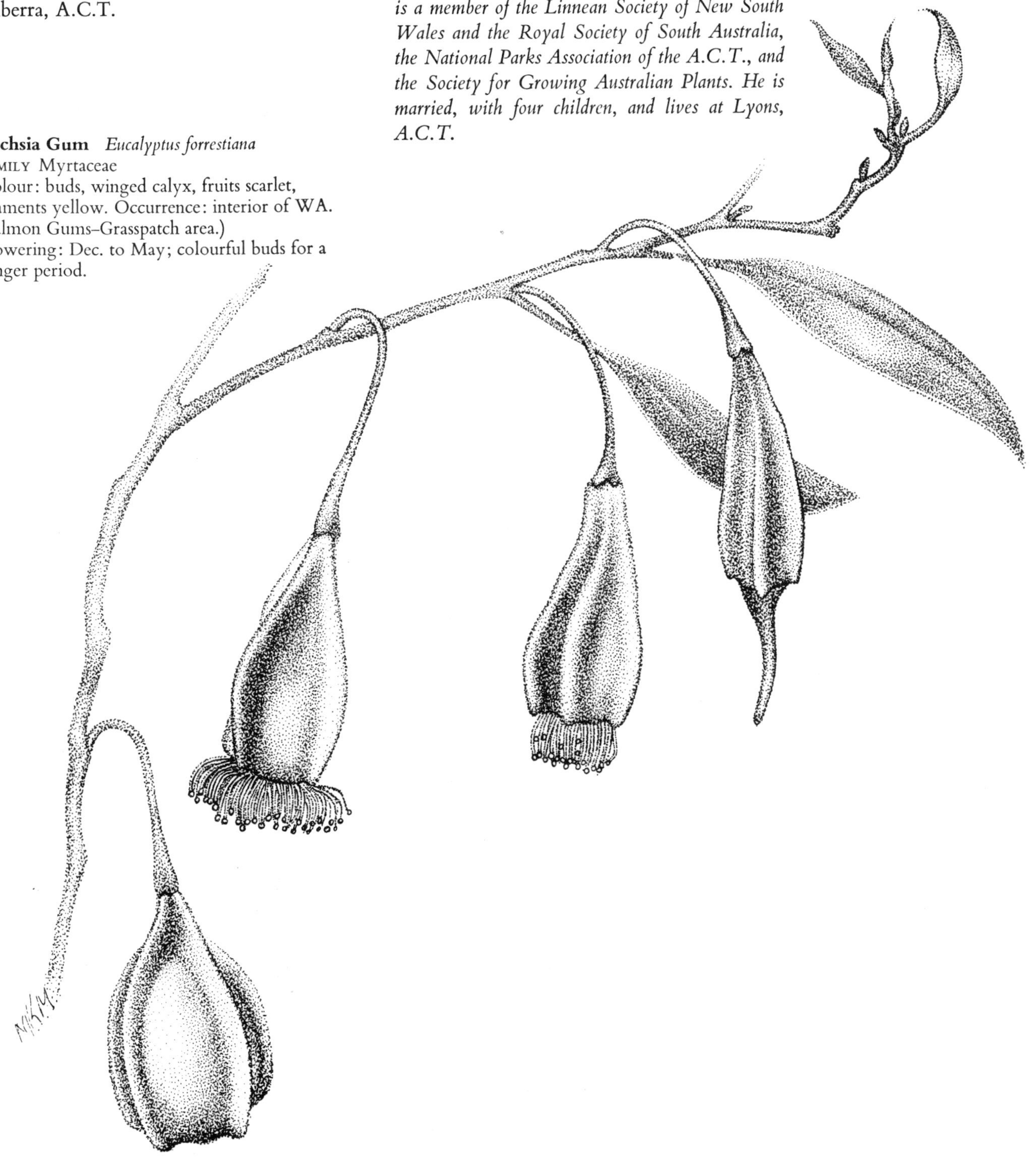

George Chippendale, B.Sc. was born in Sydney in 1921. He was educated mainly at the Paddington Public School in Sydney, and after war service in the islands north of Australia, he matriculated and attended the University of Sydney. From 1936 to 1950, excluding war service, he was the herbarium assistant at the National Herbarium of New South Wales, Sydney. After graduation, from 1950 to 1954, he was a botanist at the same herbarium. From mid-1954 to mid-1966 he was the resident botanist for the Northern Territory Administration, at Alice Springs, and since 1966 he has been the taxonomic botanist in the Forestry and Timber Bureau, Canberra. Mr Chippendale has had many papers published on aspects of plants in central Australia, and was the editor of the book Eucalyptus Buds and Fruits *(1968) and co-author with R. D. Johnston of the text for the book* Eucalypts *featuring paintings by Stan Kelly. Mr Chippendale is a member of the Linnean Society of New South Wales and the Royal Society of South Australia, the National Parks Association of the A.C.T., and the Society for Growing Australian Plants. He is married, with four children, and lives at Lyons, A.C.T.*

55

NATIONAL PARKS AND WILDFLOWER RESERVES

AYERS ROCK–MT OLGA NATIONAL PARK
276 m. SW of Alice Springs, south-west NT.

Flat or undulating country, Mulga scrub, sand ridges with Desert Oaks (*Casuarina*). Massed wildflowers in early spring if sufficient rain: many 'everlastings' (*Compositae*), parakeelyas (*Calandrinia*) and *Eremophila* species.

CAPE RANGE NATIONAL PARK
On North-west Cape, WA.

HAMERSLEY RANGES NATIONAL PARK
North-western WA, near Wittenoom.

Rugged ranges (with spectacular scenery) in arid spinifex country: white-trunked gums, Corkwoods (*Hakea lorea*), shrubs such as *Gossypium robinsonii*, *Acacia pyrifolia*, and many smaller plants including Sturt Desert Pea, various *Ptilotus* and *Eremophila* species.

National parks in the Macdonnell Ranges, eastwards and westwards of Alice Springs:

ELLERY CREEK GORGE NATIONAL PARK
50 m. W of Alice Springs.

EMILY GAP AND JESSIE GAP SCENIC RESERVES
7 m. SE of Alice Springs.

GLEN HELEN NATIONAL PARK
81 m. W of Alice Springs.

GREEN VALLEY SCENIC RESERVE
54 m. E of Alice Springs.

ORMISTON GORGE NATIONAL PARK
72 m. W of Alice Springs.

TREPHINA GORGE NATIONAL PARK
46 m. E of Alice Springs.

Gorges through the Macdonnell Ranges cut by tributaries of the Finke and Todd rivers: vividly coloured cliffs, river pools, ghost gums. A variety of shrubs on rocky ranges including the Rock Isotome (*Isotoma petrae*), Tecoma (*Pandorea doratoxylon*), Blue Pincushion (*Brunonia australis*), and the Pink Mulla Mulla (*Ptilotus helipteroides*). The more spectacular wildflower displays will be seen on plains beside and between the parallel ridges of the Macdonnells, mainly along roads leading to the scenic features of the ranges. If winter rains have been sufficient there will be massed displays of many of the 'paper daisy' species (*Compositae*): the White Paper Daisy (*Helipterum floribundum*), *Podolepis canescens*, and the Orange Immortelle (*Waitzia accuminata*).

Contains palms (*Livistona mariae*), a cycad (*Macrozamia*) and a number of species of ferns and mosses which are relics of a wetter central Australian climate.

PALM VALLEY FAUNA AND FLORA RESERVE
76 m. W of Alice Springs to Hermannsburg then 12 m. S (4-wheel-drive).

SIMPSON DESERT NATIONAL PARKS (SA AND QLD)
Extreme SW corner of Qld and adjoining part of SA.

Largely sandhill desert; vegetation of sparse grass, low scrub, scattered Desert Oaks and other trees in places. Massed wildflower displays after good rain: Yellow-top (*Senecio gregori*) and many others of the family Compositae are predominant.

TANAMI DESERT WILDLIFE SANCTUARY
200 m. NW from Alice Springs.

Mainly spinifex country with scattered shrubs such as Desert Grevillea (*Grevillea juncifolia*), *Hibiscus brachclaenus*, *Hibiscus sturti*, and *Gossypium sturtianum*.

Tall Yellow-Top *Senecio magnificus*
and
White Paper-Daisy *Helipterum floribundum*
FAMILY Compositae
A profusion of wildflowers is possible in the centre after good winter rains. The *Senecio* is a robust perennial up to 3 ft tall, with stout stems, blue-green leaves, and composite flower heads in wide corymbs. The *Helipterum* is an annual herb to 6 in., with narrow grey-green leaves and small flower heads on stem tips. Flowering time is July to Sept.

Poached-Egg Daisy *Myriocephalus stuartii*
FAMILY Compositae
A many-stemmed herbaceous plant with hairy, grey-green leaves. Each flat compound flower head, made up of many small yellow heads, is contained within an encircling ring of white bracts. This everlasting is widely distributed on sandy soils through central Australia and inland parts of NSW, SA, Vic, and WA. Flowering time is Aug. to Oct., after rains.

Minuria *Minuria leptophylla*
FAMILY Compositae
Below the rounded red sandstone domes of Mt Olga, low bushy Minuria shrubs are so densely covered with flowers that the foliage is completely hidden. Flowers have small yellow centres with long radiating rays white to lilac; leaves are very narrow. Occurs on sandy soils of the centre and inland WA. Flowering time is July to Oct.

Golden Everlasting *Helichrysum bracteatum*
FAMILY Compositae
An erect perennial widely distributed throughout central Australia and extending to the east coast, southern states and the west. Flower heads are large, with prominent involucral bracts stiff and glossy, of rich yellow sometimes bronzed. There are numerous forms—*H. albidum*, of south-west WA, which has white or rose-tinted bracts, or the sticky *H. viscosum*. Flowering time is Aug. to Sept.

Tecoma *Pandorea doratoxylon*
FAMILY Bigoniaceae
A shrub with twining, vine-like branches. Leaves are pinnate, with leaflets small, lanceolate, light green. Flowers are tubular, velvet-hairy in the throat, with 4 stamens in the tube, and borne on short racemes. The fruit is an enlarged capsule which splits to release winged seeds. It favours rocky areas through central Australia to mid-western Australia. Flowering time is Aug. to Oct.

Large-Fruited Mallee *Eucalyptus pyriformis*
FAMILY Myrtaceae
A shrub or small mallee with numerous stems reaching 4 to 15 ft high. Mature leaves are petiolate, broadly lanceolate, up to 5 in. long. Bark light brown, smooth. Flowers in umbels of 3, very large, with filaments of crimson, creamy-white or yellow. Fruits are large (up to $2\frac{1}{2}$ in. diam.) It occurs near the central-w coast of WA, extending well inland, and also in the western interior of SA. Flowering time April to Nov.

Orange Immortelle *Waitzia accuminata*
FAMILY Compositae
The *Myriocephalus* is described on page 00. The
Orange Immortelle has broad-linear leaves,
rolled-in along their margins; flower heads are
covered in orange-yellow bracts, and arranged
in corymbs. In dry sandy parts of NSW, Vic,
SA, NT, WA. Flowering time is Aug. to Oct.
(*Waitzia*).

Thick-Leaved Mallee *Eucalyptus pachyphylla*
FAMILY Myrtaceae
A low shrubby mallee, which under natural
conditions forms dense thickets. Leaves are
thick, lanceolate to ovate, almost 4 in. long.
The very large flowers are in groups of 3,
and have bud cap decoratively ribbed. Grows
in far north-western Qld and the NT.
Flowering time is May to June.

A 'Poverty Bush' *Eremophila gilesii*
FAMILY Myoporaceae
Eremophila ('desert-loving') is a widespread
genus of more than 100 species. Flowers have a
tubular, lobed corolla and a bell-shaped calyx
that remains on the fruit after the corolla has
fallen. This low shrub, has long fine sticky
leaves, and flowers about 1 in. long. It occurs in
arid mulga country, central Australia to the
central-west of WA. Flowering time is July to
Sept.

Small Pink Mulla Mulla *Ptilotus helipteroides*
FAMILY Amaranthaceae
Beneath Mt Olga's red domes grow these
fluffy-papery flowers of the type known as
'mulla mulla', 'featherhead', or 'lambs' tails'.
They belong to a genus of more than 100 species,
scattered through the dry interior of all states
except Tas. Flowering time is winter, spring,
summer.

Coral Gum *Eucalyptus torquata*
FAMILY Myrtaceae
Colour: filaments pink or scarlet; buds and
fruits usually suffused with orange or red.
Occurrence: stony hills, red soils, Coolgardie-
Norseman area, inland WA.
Flowering: Nov. to Jan.

Grevillea dryandri
FAMILY Proteaceae
A low, spreading shrub which forms exception-
ally long racemes, 9 in. to 1 ft long, carrying a
hundred or more red to creamy-white flowers.
Stems are dark, glossy, glaucous surfaced.
Leaves are much divided, with very fine
segments. Occurs in gravelly spinifex-woodlands
of the northern-inland NT. Flowering time is
June to Sept.

Western Desert Rose *Gossypium robinsonii*
FAMILY Malvaceae
Gossypium flowers have an epicalyx composed of 3 floral bracts, and dark oil glands on leaves and stem, distinguishing them from closely related *Hibiscus*, *Alyogyne* and other general which have more than 3 bracts and (except *Thespesia*) no oil glands. *Gossypium robinsonii* can be recognised by its distinctive leaves, which are deeply divided into 3 to 5 pointed lobes. It is native to dry river beds of arid north-west WA around the Hamersley Ranges. It flowers in winter to early spring.

Petalostyles *Petalostyles labichioides* var. *cassiodes*
FAMILY Caesalpiniaceae
A small shrub with distinctive pinnate leaves made up of as many as 40 pointed, half-inch leaflets. Flowers are similar to *Cassias*, and almost 1 in. across. Seeds are contained within flat, one-inch-long pods. Occurs on red sandy soil, spinifex country, through central Australia to north-west of WA. Flowering time is May to Nov.

Lemon-Flowered Gum
Eucalyptus woodwardi × *torquata*
FAMILY Myrtaceae
Eucalyptus hybridize readily when grown outside their natural habitats. This is thought to be a hybrid between *E. woodwardi* and *E. torquata*. It appears closer to *woodwardi*, which is a rather tall, yellow-flowered tree with thick, rigid glaucous leaves and axillary 3 to 6 flowered umbels. Both *woodwardi* and *torquata* are native to the Coolgardie district, interior of WA. Flowering time is Aug. to Nov.

Sturt's Desert Rose *Gossypium sturtianum*
FAMILY Malvaceae
A shrub with smooth oval or rounded leaves noticeably dotted with oil glands, which continue onto stems as black spots. Flowers are hibiscus-like. This *Gossypium*, the floral emblem of the NT, occurs on stony ground through central Australia, extending to the interior of NSW, Qld, WA, and SA. Flowering time is winter to spring.

Rock Isotome *Isotoma petraea*
FAMILY Lobeliaceae
This *Isotoma*, which grows in rugged central Australian ranges, canyons and gorges, is a perennial herb about 1 ft high. The delicate flowers, pale blue, lilac or white, have a tubular corolla with 5 pointed spreading lobes. Propagation can be from seeds or cuttings. Flowering time is June to Nov.

Eremophila obovata
FAMILY Myoporaceae
A shrub with small broad-oval leaves that taper towards the stem (obovate). Leaves, stem buds and flower calyces are densely hairy-felted giving the whole plant a grey-green appearance. Occurs in central NT: Barrow Creek. Flowering time is July to Oct.

White Paper Daisy *Helipterum floribundum* ▶
FAMILY Compositae
A massed display of *Helipterum* and other transient annuals on plains below the Macdonnell Ranges near Alice Springs. If winter rains fail, the centre is without such vast expanses of wildflowers. This paper daisy grows quickly after rain, and may flower when only a few inches high. Flowering time is July to Sept.

Eremophila duttoni
FAMILY Myoporaceae
A shrub or low tree to 10 ft, occurring in the red soils of central to mid-western Australia. Leaves are small, lanceolate. The flower's 5 petals are united to form a tubular corolla, 5-lobed at the outer end. Propagation is easiest by cuttings, as seed is difficult to germinate. Flowering time is Aug. to Dec.

Podolepis canescens
FAMILY Compositae
A tall annual herb with fine leaves and solitary, terminal flower heads on slender branched stems. The outer ray-florets of these composite heads have narrow yellow ligules, branched at their outer ends; these radiate in great number around the heads. Widely distributed through the interior, as far as the Kimberleys and the inland south-west. Flowering time is April to Oct.

Round-leaved Parakeelya   *Calandrinia remo*
FAMILY Portulacaceae
A low, clump-forming succulent annual or perennial distinguished by its cylindrical fleshy leaves. Flowers up to 1 in. diameter, on slender stems. It occurs on deep red sands or in *Acacia* scrub country of the centre, NT and SA. Flowering winter and summer.

Blue Pincushion   *Brunonia australis*
FAMILY Brunoniaceae
This small herb, the only species of its genus, occurs over most of the continent except the tropical north coast and forested regions. Slender stems carry small flower heads about 1 in. across. From each of the small blue florets that make up a head protrude long yellow-tipped styles—the 'pins' in the 'cushion'. Flowering time is Aug. to Oct.

Hibiscus sturtii
FAMILY Malvaceae
An erect shrub 2 or 3 ft high, leaves small, broadly ovate. Stems, leaves, and calyx densely covered with short, fine hairs, giving a hoary grey-green appearance. Flowers small, lilac to deep pink. Grows in rocky country through central Australia, extending to north-west WA. Flowering time is Sept. to Nov.

Eremophila calorhabdos
FAMILY Myoporaceae
A slender shrub 4 to 6 ft tall, with crowded ovate-lanceolate leaves. Stems, especially towards the extremities, are white, densely covered with short white hairs. The deep-pink to magenta tubular flowers appear in considerable numbers on the leaf axils a few inches below the stem tips. Occurs in red sand country west of the Nullarbor Plains (Eyre District), WA. Flowering time is Sept. to Feb.

Grevillea refracta ▶
FAMILY Proteaceae
A tall shrub, leaves divided and segments narrow-lanceolate. Flowers in short, one-sided racemes, not conspicuous at a distance; perianth tube curved, finely hirsute, style short. Occurs across northern parts of this central Australian region. Flowering time is April to June.

Sturt Desert Pea *Clianthus formosus*
FAMILY Papilionaceae
A low trailing annual or biennial herbaceous plant, leaves pinnate, silky, giving whole plant a grey-green appearance. Flowers hang vertically in radiating umbel-like racemes on erect flower stems. Colour is usually brilliant red, with glossy black or sometimes deep maroon centre. Widely distributed through the dry interior of Qld, NSW, SA, NT, and WA. Flowering time is July to Jan.

Yellow-Top *Senecio gregori*
FAMILY Compositae
At the western edge of the Simpson Desert these prolific annuals brighten countless miles of red sandhills whenever winter rains reach this far inland. Flower heads are composite structures of central bisexual disc-florets, surrounded by ray-florets with inch-long radiating petal-like ligules. Widespread through central Australia, reaching to the central west coast of WA. Flowering time is July to Sept.

Desert Grevillea *Grevillea juncifolia*
FAMILY Myrtaceae
A spectacular tall shrub with brilliant orange flowers borne in great numbers on long racemes. Leaves are long, needle-like, with two grooves along the undersurface. It grows on red-sand spinifex plains through central Australia and westwards to the arid north-west coast of WA. Flowering time is Aug. to Nov.

Kingsmill's Mallee *Eucalyptus kingsmillii*
FAMILY Myrtaceae
A multi-stemmed mallee or small tree 6 to 20 ft high, with rough trunk, smooth branches and lanceolate leaves. The filaments of the large flowers vary from creamy-yellow to red, while operculum and calyx have 8 prominent ridges. Occurs in sandy and stony country, Fortescue and Ashburton districts, north-west WA. Flowering time is June to Sept.

Hibiscus brachyclaenus
FAMILY Malvaceae
A slender shrub to 3 ft, with densely hirsute branches, foliage, buds and flower calyces. Leaves are small, slender-ovate, serrate-edged, with grey-green felted surfaces. Flowers rather small, pink to violet with crimson centres. Occurs in rocky country of inland NT extending westwards to north-west and Kimberleys of WA. Flowering time is April to Oct.

Cattle Bush *Trichodesma zeylanicum*
FAMILY Boraginaceae
Widespread through northern, mid-western and central Australia, this is an erect, herbaceous shrub to 6 ft tall, carrying abundant blue, sometimes white, flowers, which have anthers cohering to form a white central column. Flowering time is Sept. to Dec.

The vegetation of Northern Australia is a complex mixture of typically Australian species, and species which either occur in tropical South-East Asia, or which have obvious affinities with species which grow there. Remarkably few of the Australian species actually occur in the southern temperate parts of the continent. The vast arid interior of Australia has for a long time acted as an effective barrier so that a northern tropical flora has evolved which is distinctly different at the specific level to the southern vegetation. The vegetation of North Australia is of great interest and importance for two reasons. Firstly it demonstrates the adaptation of the Australian flora to a tropical environment. Secondly it shows the adaptive and competitive ability of plants obviously originating outside Australia, as they grow alongside Australian species in the Australian environment.

Structurally and floristically, the vegetation of Northern Australia is very similar right across the country, from the North-West coast of Western Australia to the east coast of the Gulf of Carpentaria. The unifying feature throughout the region is the climate. A brief description of the climate is therefore essential, to enable the reader to see the vegetation in its right perspective.

The climate is one of summer rainfall and winter drought. The amount of summer rainfall is highest in the far north (Darwin 60") and progressively less further south and inland (Katherine 35"). Similarly the summer growing season is longest in the far north, and shorter further from the coast. Conversely the dry winter period is shorter in the north. Ninety percent of the rainfall is recorded from November to March. Summer temperatures are high throughout, with the sea exerting a moderating influence close to the coast. Temperatures of over 100°F are common inland. The summers are also characteristically very humid. The winters are warm and dry—maximum winter temperatures are in the low eighties, and the thermometer rarely falls below 40°F even far from the coast. Frosts therefore are virtually unknown. The rate of evaporation is high throughout, and day-length does not vary markedly through the year.

The four seasons as recognised in temperate regions do not exist. There is a wet season and a dry season, with two indeterminate changeover periods, which are the hottest times of the year. It is interesting to note, however, that a large proportion of the woody species in the north are deciduous (including many of the Eucalypts). They lose their leaves during the dry season, an obvious mechanism for surviving the period of greatest physiological stress. However, new leaves begin to appear long before there has been any hint of rain, at the time of the year

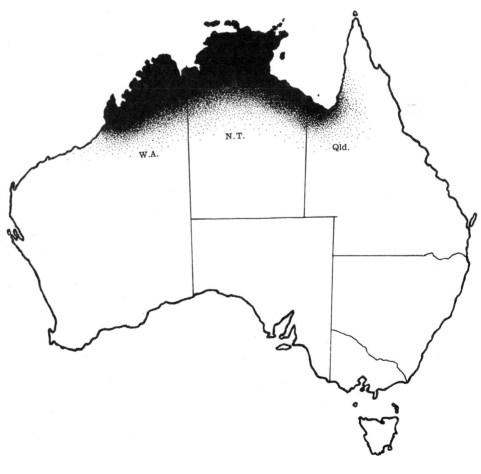

which would correspond roughly with the spring season of the temperate zone.

There is one other feature of the dry season which is of undoubted importance in the evolution of the vegetation, namely fire. Fire is probably a natural phenomenon in this environment, although its incidence would undoubtedly have increased with the arrival of aboriginal man, and later, the European settlers. Apart from isolated fire-sheltered areas, the whole of the country is burned regularly. The vegetation is not only fire-tolerant but seems to be actually adapted to the regular occurrence of grass fires.

Having so far considered the area of Northern Australia as a whole, it is now proposed to look at a few vegetation types in greater detail, in order to show the importance of soil factors on the distribution of plant species within the area. Particularly significant factors are soil textures, drainage status and the availability of water during the dry season. The 'Top End' of the Northern Territory is still the most accessible part of Northern Australia and thus is the area most likely to command the attention of Australian wildflower enthusiasts. The vegetation of the 'Top End' with its generally higher rainfall shows the affinities with the South-East Asian vegetation more clearly than the drier areas further inland and to the east and west.

By far the greatest part of the region is dominated by Eucalypts with a tropical tall grass understory. In general, the grasses are annuals on the sandier soils and perennials on the loamier soils. In the very far north there are areas of Eucalypt forest without tall grasses. In the dry season it is the trees and shrubs which provide the greatest attraction, for this is the season of their flowering. Of the Eucalypts, *Eucalyptus miniata* (Woollybutt) with its bright orange flowers, *E. phoenicea* with orange flowers and yellow bark, and *E. setosa* with bright red flowers are the most attractive.

Many of the smaller trees and shrubs are extremely colourful at various times through the dry season. *Cochlospermum fraseri* (Kapok bush) has large yellow flowers reminiscent of buttercups; *Brachychiton paradoxum* has clusters of pink waxy flowers pressed closely to the branches; *Planchonia careya* with its pink filamentous flowers, and *Buchanania obovata* in the Mango family Anacaridiaceae, with its sprays of white flowers, are both common throughout the area. Of the Grevilleas one of the commonest and most attractive is *Grevillea heliosperma* with bright red flowers. Another very common tropical genus is *Terminalia*, member of the very widespread tropical family Combretaceae; generally these do not have particularly striking flowers, but *T. grandiflora* has masses of beautiful delicate white flowers. Quite common in the lower rainfall areas are the leguminous Coral Tree, *Erythrina vespertilio*, with scarlet flowers, and *Hakea cunninghamii*, with very striking white bottle-brush flowers. In the wetter parts *Xanthostemon paradoxum* with bright yellow flowers is common. This is a myrtaceous genus not found in the temperate parts of Australia. The freshness of the new leaves of many of the deciduous trees and shrubs provides welcome relief from the parched and fire blackened scene towards the end of the dry season. Particularly noteworthy in this respect are the stately leguminous Ironwood, *Erythrophleum chlorostachys*, the small Zamia Palm, *Cycas media* and the Fan Palm, *Livistona humilis*. The new leaves of some of the Eucalypts, notably *Eucalyptus clavigera* and *E. confertiflora* are often the most lovely shades of russet brown and purple. Another splash of colour is provided by the Salmon Gum, *E. alba*, the bark of which changes from white to blood-red with changes in seasons.

The herbaceous flora of the Eucalypt woodlands and forests is at its most interesting towards the end of the wet season. Then the grass is tall and dense so that everything is obscured. However, excursions into the long grass, particularly on sandy soils in the north, and on granite soils, prove most rewarding. Some of the many and varied plants to be found are various species of *Hibiscus*, the scarlet creeping *Grevillea goodii*, the strange *Tacca leontopetaloides*, the little blue pincushions, *Borreria leptoloba*, creeping *Hibbertia cistifolia*, and *Clerodendrum holtzei*, the minute delicate *Cleome tetrandra*, *Polygala* spp and *Mitrasacme* spp and many bright red and pink everlastings, of which *Polycarpaea longiflora* and *Gomphrena canescens* are the most frequent.

Throughout the general Eucalypt bush country there occur frequent more open sandy drainage flats. Here are often found the stately *E. polycarpa*, the beautiful *Grevillea pteridifolia* with orange flowers, the northern Banksia, *B. dentata* and the delicate white flowered *Verticordia cunninghamii*. However, it is the wealth of small and delicate herbaceous plants that makes these areas of special interest to the botanist. Although many of the genera occurring in these areas are shared with southern Australia, there are some, notably *Cartonema*, *Commelina*, and *Lindernia*, which are found solely in the north. Of the many other attractive flowers to be found the following are worthy of mention: *Xyris complanata*, *Thysanotus* spp, *Sowerbaea alliaceae*, *Utricularia chrysantha*, *Stylidium* spp, *Mimulus linearis*, *Lobelia dioica*, *Drosera petiolaris* and *Byblis liniflora*.

The sub-coastal plains of Northern Australia may be best known for their buffaloes and aquatic bird life. They are also areas of special interest to the botanist. The black cracking-clay plains themselves are floristically dull, except to students of sedges and swamp grasses. They are annually inundated, lush and green in the wet season and parched and dry in the dry season. Along the muddy banks of the estuaries of the major rivers is found one of the most beautiful flowers in the north—*Acanthus ilicifolius* which is of special interest to botanists, in that it is the only species of *Acanthus* found native in Australia. For the botanist the inland fringes of the plains provide the greatest interest. Here are found extensive areas of monsoon forest and thicket, where practically all species have Asian rather than Australian affinities. There are many waterholes with the attractive floating plants, *Nymphoides geminatum* and *Nelumbo nucifera* in the centre, and fringed with the deep *Monochoria cyanea* and *Utricularia flexuosa*. Frequently associated with these waterholes is the fresh-water mangrove, *Barringtonia gracilis* with its bright red hanging spikes of filamentous flowers. Scattered around the sub-coastal plains are extensive areas of tall Paperbark, *Melaleuca* spp, swamps. These paperbarks are the habitat for the delicate epiphytic orchid *Dendrobium canaliculatum*. Often on the drier margins of these swamps are found banks of the beautiful purple *Dysophila verticillata*. Another fascinating vegetation type in this region is the Pandanus thicket, seen at its best in the wet season, when there is an abundance of small herbs in the short grass.

Northern Australia is a vast but thinly populated area. It might therefore be thought that there is little need for conservation of the flora at this time. This thought is far from the truth. Much of the area is still in almost its virgin state. For this reason alone, there is justification in creating reserves now, and fortunately for Australia the government recognises this need. The whole of Cobourg Peninsula is a sanctuary. There are plans afoot to establish a large national park on the western fringe of the Arnhem Land Aboriginal Reserve to include parts of the Arnhem Land escarpment country, and sub-coastal plains. The most pressing need for flora conservation at present is in the immediate vicinity of Darwin. In the near future there will probably be the same need around any of the major developing areas, such as Gove and Kununurra. There are many fine examples of natural rainforest close to Darwin particularly along the shore lines, and in isolated pockets inland, such as Holmes Jungle.

C. S. Robinson,
Ecologist,
Northern Territory Administration,
Darwin, N.T.

Mr C. S. Robinson was born in England in 1941. He graduated from Cambridge University in 1963 with B.A. (Hons) and Dip. Agric. He studied Natural Sciences, including Botany for his degree and then changed to Agriculture for a postgraduate diploma.

He emigrated to Australia at the end of 1963 and soon found himself in Darwin. He worked for 18 months as the taxonomic botanist with the Agriculture Branch, and then joined the South Australian Department of Agriculture as an Arid Zone Ecologist. Early in 1967 he returned to the Northern Territory as an Ecologist with the Land Resources Section of the Primary Industries Branch.

His main interest in the botanical field is the study of plant associations in relation to soil and climatic factors and the use of certain species as indicators of land use potential. He is keen to see that the inevitable development of the Northern Territory is based on sound conservation principles.

Seaside Mahoe *Thespesia populnea*
FAMILY Malvaceae
Colour: yellow, fading orange-brown.
Occurrence: north coast (maritime) NT, Qld, WA. Flowering: Mar. to June.

NATIONAL PARKS AND WILDFLOWER RESERVES

COBOURG PENINSULA SANCTUARY
N coast of NT, NE of Darwin; access by air or sea.

Savannah woodland and tropical monsoon forest, extensive mangrove forests (swamps) along peninsula's southern coast.

DALY RIVER SANCTUARY
On NW coast of NT. at mouth of Daly River.

Coastal lowlands, swamps, tropical layered forest; entry restricted.

EDITH FALLS NATIONAL PARK
35 m. N of Katherine then 18 m. E from Stuart Hwy.

River pools and falls surrounded by Pandanus palms, lush vegetation through gorges; orange-flowered *Eucalyptus miniata* and orange-yellow *Grevillea pteridifolia*.

GEIKIE GORGE NATIONAL PARK
Far north of WA (Kimberley region) close to Fitzroy Crossing.

A long, colourful gorge on the Fitzroy River, Pandanus palms, melaleucas, *Passiflora* vines, yellow *Cochlospermum heteroneurum* on ranges.

KATHERINE GORGE NATIONAL PARK
22 m. E of Katherine (220 m. S of Darwin).

Magnificent river gorge with Pandanus, *Grevillea pteridifolia*, and on ranges, *Eucalyptus miniata*, *Cochlospermum gregori*.

MURGANELLA SANCTUARY
N coast NT. between Cobourg Peninsula and Oenpelli mission. Access very difficult.

Tropical layered forest, extensive mangroves. North-coast flora includes species such as *Nymphaea gigantea*, *Nelumbo nucifera*, *Nymphoides geminatum*, *Eucalyptus phoenicea*, *Thespesia populnea* and *Xantostemon paradoxus*.

PRINCE REGENT RIVER RESERVE (soon to be a national park)
On the Kimberley coast about 170 m. NE of Derby; access extremely difficult.

Extremely spectacular rugged country with huge river gorge. Tropical woodland on sandstone. High rainfall, rich tropical vegetation near coast.

WINDJANA GORGE (proposed national park)
Kimberleys of WA 80 m. E of Derby.

Spectacular gorge through limestone ranges (former barrier reef), 300 ft cliffs. Dry-season flora includes the pink-flowered *Brachychiton viscidulum*, and the yellow *Cochlospermum heteroneurum*.

WOOLWONGA WILDLIFE SANCTUARY
E of Darwin, on swamps of Alligator R.

Extensive swamps and lagoons, paperbarks (*Melaleuca*), Waterlilies (*Nymphaea*, *Nelumbo*), Swamp Bloodwood (*Eucalyptus ptchocarpa*) and species of *Utricularia*.

Swamp Bloodwood *Eucalyptus ptychocarpa*
FAMILY Myrtaceae
Colour: crimson, pink or white.
Occurrence: 'top end' of NT, Kimberleys of WA. Flowering: Jan. to May.

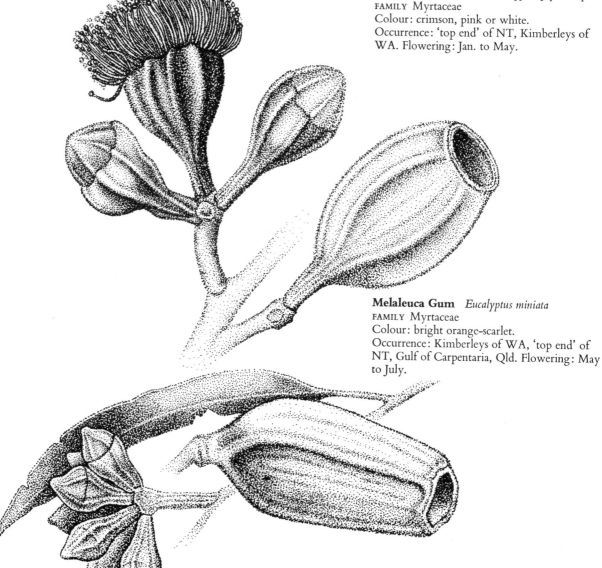

Melaleuca Gum *Eucalyptus miniata*
FAMILY Myrtaceae
Colour: bright orange-scarlet.
Occurrence: Kimberleys of WA, 'top end' of NT, Gulf of Carpentaria, Qld. Flowering: May to July.

THE NORTH-EAST

The vegetation of north-eastern Australia is rich and varied. Along its tidal flats are extensive mangroves; on its coastal plains are swamp forests, areas of savannah and a type of vegetation known as 'wallum'; along its ranges are hardwood forests, rainforests and, on the highest peaks, even cloud forests; across the western slopes are again some hardwood forests, and extensive savannah plains.

In some places along Australia's tropical north-eastern coast, in estuaries and sheltered bays subject to tidal flooding, the pockets of mangrove forest may be many square miles in extent. These tropical mangroves consist of a great number of species of extremely diverse form, making a vegetation belt completely different in visual character and plant species to any other in this region. While most trees are small a few species develop to a commercially useful size. Barks of the mangroves range from smooth to rough, from startling white to jet black, and the leaves from pale to very dark green. With their characteristic tangle of arched aerial roots the mangroves create a bizarre, often weird effect. In places, where they are not too close-packed, these trees are hosts to numerous epiphytes, such as ferns, orchids, and vines like the *Hoya*; in a few places, *Nipa* palms occur.

Where the coastline is windswept or sandy the first line of vegetation varies from heathland (particularly in southern parts of this region) to stunted forest. The heathlands consist of a few low trees and *Pandanus* palms, interspersed with shrubs of many families. Succulents occur in small numbers, and there are some terrestrial orchids.

Saline swamps occur where the coastal lands are low-lying, and are backed by intermittent freshwater swamplands. In the southern areas these favour the growth of *Casuarina glauca*, and some of the larger species of *Melaleuca*. However, in the tropics *Casuarina* does not occur, being replaced by *Pandanus* and *Dillenia*.

Where trees are scarce or completely lacking, there is often a dense growth of giant sedges (sword-grass). Here again, on some trees, there are epiphytes in considerable number; it is, however, rather surprising that sago palms do not occur in the north-eastern coastal swamplands.

The northern coastal plains are often surprising to visitors from the south who expect to find lush rainforests everywhere. In fact, most of the country is flat, the soil either very poor schist, or sandy, favouring 'wallum' vegetation. Here the trees are stunted, and predominantly of the family *Myrtaceae*. This wallum vegetation occurs even in areas where the rainfall is comparatively high.

In some areas where soil, terrain and rainfall are suitable, especially between the Herbert and Endeavour rivers, there were once extensive tracts of lowland rainforest. But now these coastal jungles, except for a few small pockets, have been cleared for agricultural purposes. It is to be hoped that the few remaining small areas will be preserved as inviolable national parks or similar reserves. These lowland rainforests were once the habitat of numerous epiphytes, and a variety of shrubs grew along their borders.

The mountain ranges, both coastal and Great Divide, from northern NSW to the tip of Cape York Peninsula, are probably less spoilt than other parts of this region. Nevertheless there have been serious inroads into the vegetation of the ranges for agricultural, pastoral and to a lesser extent, forestry purposes; fires are also taking a heavy toll.

Extensive rainforests occur, usually interspersed with areas of hardwood forest, where rainfall is high and the soil is rich. Elsewhere, with insufficient rainfall to permit rainforest, there is either hardwood forest or savannah woodland. Considerable areas of the mountain rainforests are in national parks or reserves, including a large tract between Cardwell and Cooktown.

On some of the highest peaks a type of cloud forest occurs, containing species of orchid, ferns and other flora found nowhere else in Australia.

In the mountain rainforests there are many epiphytic orchids, as well as a few terrestrial orchids, of New Guinea–Malayan affinities, while in pockets of hardwood forest within rainforest regions, even in the tropics, there are many flowering shrubs and terrestrial orchids belonging to genera common in temperate Australia.

Cape York Peninsula is of special interest biologically in that it is the channel through which most of the recent species exchanges between New Guinea and Australia were made. It appears that in recent times New Guinea has contributed many rainforest species to Australia (while Australia has supplied a number of woodland species to New Guinea.) For example, it is on the summits of some of the peninsula's highest mountains that are found Australia's only representatives of such New Guinea plants as *Rhododendron*, *Balanops*, *Bubbia*, and *Agapetes*.

Large areas of savannah exist also, particularly on Cape York. Grasses flourish, and where dense exclude all other small plants. Elsewhere, with grass less luxuriant, a wide variety of flowering plants, belonging to a number of families, appear in seasonal abundance.

On the drier western slopes of the northern Great Dividing Range the ground cover is usually of the savannah type, with pockets of hardwood forest. If granite soil is associated with this savannah the grass becomes sparse, and it is here that many small plants are to be seen at their best. At flowering time such areas are richly rewarding to the botanist and to anyone interested in this region's diverse flora.

A. W. Dockrill,
Curator,
Orchid Herbarium,
Lae, TPNG.

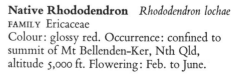

Native Rhododendron *Rhododendron lochae*
FAMILY Ericaceae
Colour: glossy red. Occurrence: confined to summit of Mt Bellenden-Ker, Nth Qld, altitude 5,000 ft. Flowering: Feb. to June.

A. W. Dockrill was born in Sydney in 1915, and at the age of twelve began a lifelong interest in orchids under the guidance of E. L. Hayes. This interest deepened and received valuable direction some years later when he developed friendships with P. A. Gilbert, the Rev. H. M. R. Rupp, D. P. Vermeulen, and Dr R. E. Holtlum. These authorities were responsible for much of his basic knowledge, and encouraged him to undertake a serious (though still amateur) study of Australia's indigenous orchids.

In 1957 he moved to Cairns, where he was able to study orchids and other flora of tropical north-eastern Australia. In 1967 he took up the position of Keeper of the Herbarium at the Lae herbarium in New Guinea.

His first published paper appeared in The Australian Orchid Review of March 1954. Since then he has had more than seventy botanical papers published in the Journal of Orchidology, Victorian Naturalist, Australian Orchid Review, North Queensland Naturalist, The Orchadian, Orcheen, and Australian Plants. A. W. Dockrill has had two books published: Australian Sarcanthenae (1967), and Volume 1 of a large and authoritative work, Australian Indigenous Orchids (1969).

Bulbophyllum elisae
FAMILY Orchidaceae
Colour: green streaked with red-brown.
Occurrence: coastal Qld, NSW, Vic.
Flowering: Oct. to April.

Queensland Pyramid Tree

Lagunaria patersonia

FAMILY Malvaceae
Colour: pink. Occurrence: east-coastal Qld, Norfolk and Lord Howe islands.
Flowering: Nov. to Jan.

MKM

71

NATIONAL PARKS AND WILDFLOWER RESERVES

BELLENDEN-KER NATIONAL PARK
W of Bruce Hwy between Innisfail and Cairns, final access on foot.

Contains highest mountain in Qld, 5,275 ft Mt Bartle Frere. Dense tropical rainforest varying in character according to altitude, rich in epiphytic orchids, ferns. Near the summit is the only known occurrence of Australia's one native rhododendron, *Rhododendron lochae*.
See National Parks of East Coast.

BUNYA MOUNTAINS NATIONAL PARK
CONWAY NATIONAL PARK (QLD)
NE coast via Mackay, Proserpine, to Shute Harbour.

Rugged coastal ranges with lowland rainforest, mangroves, coastal woodland, many epiphytes and flowering shrubs such as *Hibiscus diversifolius*.
See National Parks of East Coast.

CUNNINGHAM'S GAP NATIONAL PARK
CRYSTAL CREEK (MT SPEC) NATIONAL PARK
N-coast Qld, 42 m. N of Townsville to Paluma, then 13 m. E.

Upland tropical rainforest on Mt Spec (3,150 ft), hardwood forests.

DORRIGO STATE PARK
DUNK ISLAND NATIONAL PARK
3 m. off coast opposite Tully, 120 m. N of Townsville.

See National Parks of East Coast.
Rainforest and open forest, palms.

EUNGELLA NATIONAL PARK
50 m. W of Mackay, on the Clarke Range.

Rugged ranges exceeding 4,000 ft; highland tropical rainforest extremely rich in epiphytic and terrestrial ferns, arboreal orchids, palms and tropical woodland areas.
See National Parks of East Coast.

GIBRALTAR RANGE NATIONAL PARK
HINCHINBROOK ISLAND NATIONAL PARK
Off N Qld coast midway between Townsville and Innisfail.

Mountainous, extremely rugged ranges; tropical rainforest, coastal tropical woodlands, extensive mangroves.

HOOK ISLAND NATIONAL PARK
E of Proserpine, just S of Hayman I.

A large mountainous island rising to 1,478 ft, with tropical rainforest and mixed coastal woodland.

LAKE BARRINE NATIONAL PARK
On Atherton Tableland, N Qld, 38 m. from Cairns by Gillies Hwy.

A lake in a volcanic crater, surrounded by upland tropical rainforest (altitude 2,400 ft). Many ferns on trees and ground, huge buttressed jungle figs.

LAKE EACHAM NATIONAL PARK
On Atherton Tableland close to Lake Barrine, just off Gillies Hwy.

A deep volcanic crater lake very similar to Lake Barrine; a walk track encircles the deep blue lake, tunnelling through rainforest by banks of delicate ferns.

LAMINGTON NATIONAL PARK (QLD)
MT ELLIOTT NATIONAL PARK
N Qld between Ayr and Townsville just W of Bruce Hwy.

See National Parks of East Coast.
Coastal tropical woodland, some upland tropical rainforest.

MT HYPIPAMEE (THE CRATER) NATIONAL PARK
Atherton Tableland, 15 m. S of Atherton.

Around the deep crater is magnificent rainforest (but only 900 acres) with giant trees carrying huge Staghorn ferns and many smaller ferns, orchids.

MT WINDSOR TABLELAND NATIONAL PARK
Far north-coastal Qld, NW of Mossman. Elevation 3,500 to 4,000 ft.

A magnificent, largely inaccessible wilderness region on a high plateau at northern end of Great Dividing Range; upland tropical rainforest and tropical woodland.
See National Parks of East Coast.

NEW ENGLAND NATIONAL PARK (QLD)
NOOSA NATIONAL PARK (QLD)
PALMERSTON NATIONAL PARK
Situated along Palmerston Hwy, beginning 20 m. W of Innisfail.

See National Parks of East Coast.
This road through magnificent rainforest is unsurpassed; walk tracks lead out to waterfalls set in jungle greenery, a world of mossy, buttressed softwoods, ferns and colourful fungi.

TAMBORINE MTN PARKS (QLD)
TULLY FALLS NATIONAL PARK
N Qld, Atherton Tableland, 15 m. S of Ravenshoe.

See National Parks of East Coast.
Rugged mountain country with rainforest. Falls less spectacular now that water is taken for hydro-electricity.

WALLAMAN FALLS NATIONAL PARK
W of Ingham.

Falls 900 ft high, rainforest and tropical woodland.

Swamp Bloodwood or Red Bloodwood
Eucalyptus ptychocarpa
FAMILY Myrtaceae
A medium-sized, rough-barked, highly ornamental tree, with huge leaves commonly 12 in. long and 4 in. wide. Bloodwoods are named for the red kino that exudes from lesions in the bark. Flowers are produced in large clusters (terminal, corymbose, umbels 3 to 7 flowered) varying white to crimson. This bloodwood occurs along swampy watercourses in the Kimberleys and the 'Top End' of the NT. Flowering time is mainly Jan. to Mar.

Tropical Woollybutt or **Melaleuca Gum**
Eucalyptus miniata
FAMILY Myrtaceae
This common species, often attaining 30–50 ft, is smooth-barked on branches and upper trunk, rough at the butt. Through winter it carries masses of orange-scarlet flowers. The inflorescences are both terminal and axillary. It ranges from inland Cape York and Gulf of Carpentaria to Darwin and into the Kimberleys. Flowering time is May to Aug.

Brachychiton viscidulum
FAMILY Sterculiaceae
A small tree of the Kimberleys, favouring stony ridges; common in the King Leopold, Oscar and Napier ranges. Leaves are sparse or absent at time of flowering. Flowers are arranged in large clusters of 20 or more. Individual blooms are large, 5-lobed, bell-shaped, pubescent and very sticky to touch. It flowers in the winter dry season.

A Tropical Wattle *Acacia* species
FAMILY Mimosaceae
Growing in open savannah—woodland countr near Katherine, NT, this small tree carries long flower spikes in soft golden pendant masses. Flowering time is June to July.

A Yellow Waterlily *Nymphoides geminatum*
FAMILY Nymphaeaceae
A small aquatic plant which holds yellow flowers a few inches above water level, at times in such numbers that the shallow margins of tropical swamps and billabongs become a mass of colour. The floating leaves are small and heart-shaped. This species occurs in coastal NT, and may be found close to Darwin. It flowers in the winter dry season.

Brachychiton viscidulum
FAMILY Sterculiaceae
A small tree of the Kimberleys, favouring stony ridges; common in the King Leopold, Oscar and Napier ranges. Leaves are sparse or absent at time of flowering. Flowers are arranged in large clusters of 20 or more. Individual blooms are large, 5-lobed, bell-shaped, pubescent and very sticky to touch. It flowers in the winter dry season.

A Native Hibiscus
Hibiscus zonatus var. *spinulos*
FAMILY Malvaceae
Growing in the rugged King Leopold Ranges in the Kimberleys (tropical far-northern WA). The stems carry short sharp spines which continue onto ribs of leaves and buds, which have an over-all felted layer of very fine, very short spines. The large pink flowers make this a conspicuous shrub. It flowers July to Oct or longer.

A Tropical Grevillea *Grevillea pteridifolia* ▶
FAMILY Proteaceae
The rich orange-yellow flowers make termina spikes often exceeding 6 in. in length. Leaves are pinnate, leaf-segments very narrow. This small tree (15 to 20 ft) favours creek banks and watercourses across tropical northern Australia Qld and NT. Flowering time is June to Aug.

Sesbania formosa
FAMILY Papilionaceae
A tree up to 30 ft bearing creamy-white flowers in profusion. Individual flowers are pea-shaped, exceptionally large (3 in. long) and arranged in multiple racemes forming huge conspicuous flower masses. Leaves are 1 ft. or more in length, and divided into many small leaflets. This tree occurs along watercourses of the far north and north-west of WA. Flowering time is Jan., May, July to Oct.

Ravine Orchid *Sarcochilus fitzgeraldii*
FAMILY Orchidaceae
This epiphytic orchid, the largest-flowered of its genus, grows on boulders in deep, moist rainforest gullies of the coastal ranges of northern NSW and southern Qld. Its perfumed flowers, 1 in. or more across, grow in racemes from extended stems. Leaves are long, fleshy, channelled and usually curved. Flowering time is Sept. to Jan.

Flame Tree *Brachychiton acerifolium*
FAMILY Sterculiaceae
A medium to large tree occurring in coastal rainforests northwards, from Illawarra (NSW) into Qld. Its numerous waxy scarlet bells hang in long panicles from bare branches, the leaves being dropped when the tree is in full bloom. Leaves vary from palmately lobed on young trees, to entire, and dark glossy green. Seeds form in large woody boat-shaped capsules. Flowering time is Oct. to Mar.

Gomphrena flaccida
FAMILY Amarantheaceae
A low herbaceous shrub, 1 to 3 ft tall, with branching stems. The spherical papery flower-heads are borne terminally, and are 1 to 1½ in. diameter. The genus *Gomphrena* differs from closely related and similar-looking *Trichinium* and *Ptilotus* genera in having leaves in opposite rather than alternate placement up stems. It occurs in savannah woodlands of tropical NT and the Kimberleys. Flowering time is Mar. to July.

Giant Waterlily *Nymphaea gigantea*
FAMILY Nymphaeaceae
This species commonly has flowers of blue, mauve, pink or white. Here two colour forms of the one species intermingle. Flowers may be 1 ft in diameter, the floating round or heart-shaped leaves, which have a purple undersurface, much larger. This lily occurs across tropical coastal Australia from north-east NSW to north-west WA. Flowering time is April to Oct.

Black Bean *Castanospermum australe*
FAMILY Papilionaceae
A large tree, reaching 130 ft, with long glossy pinnate leaves. Flower racemes burst out well down the branches on old wood. Containing great quantities of nectar, they are constantly visited by lorikeets. Seed pods are black, hard, heavy, 6 to 10 in. long. The Black Bean occurs on moist alluvial soil in rainforests, particularly along stream banks of Qld and north-eastern NSW. Flowering time is Oct. to Dec.

A Kurrajong *Brachychiton paradoxus* ▶
FAMILY Sterculiaceae
A small woody tree or spindly shrub, leafless at time of flowering, and seeming dead but for the very large, deep pink to crimson, open bell-shaped flowers clustered along the bare branches. New foliage appears after summer rains. Occurs in the 'Top End' of the NT. It flowers in the winter dry season.

Rock Orchid   *Dendrobium speciosum*
FAMILY Orchidaceae
From a dark green clump of thick fleshy
pseudobulbs and large stiff oval leaves rise long
racemes each carrying numerous bright golden,
cream or white flowers. Individual blooms may
be small, or up to 2 in. across. Found along the
east coast and mountains from north Qld to
Vic, on rocks, not always in rainforest. The
variety *híllii*, King Orchid, grows on trees.
Flowering time is Aug. to Oct.

Lotus Lily   *Nelumbo nucifera* ▶
FAMILY Nelumbonaceae
Growing in the deeper water of lagoons across
coastal northern Australia, lotus lilies lift huge
deep pink flowers above leaves often several fe
in diameter. Unlike the *Nymphaea* lilies, leaves
of *Nelumbo* are not always floating on the
water; most are above the surface on thick
strong stems, while roots anchor in mud where
water is 3 to 6 ft deep. It flowers in the winter
dry season.

Golden Orchid
Dendrobium discolor (syn *D. undulatum*)
FAMILY Orchidaceae
A north Qld orchid that grows on rainforest trees and rocks. In its tropical habitat the pseudobulbs may reach many feet in length, but are shorter in southern areas. Flowers are large, golden brown, with undulate petals and sepals. Flowering time is April to May.

Yellow Hibiscus *Hibiscus diversifolius* ▶
FAMILY Malvaceae
Overlooking Shute Harbour (in Conway National Park) and the Whitsunday Islands, these native hibiscus shrubs lift large deep-yellow flowers on slender swaying stems. They occur in coastal Qld and NSW. The leaves of this species are exceptionally variable, slender-ovate, broadly ovate, or 3 to 5-lobed. Flowering time is summer to autumn.

Leichhardt Bean *Cassia brewsteri* (a northern form)
FAMILY Caesalpiniaceae
In central-coastal Qld, outside the rainforests, *Cassia brewsteri* appears quite different from the southern trees. Yet, the flowers are still in long slender racemes, the leaves still long, pinnate with ovate leaflets, and the seeds borne in similar thick pods which may be up to 12 in. long. Flowering time is Oct. to Dec.

Golden Bladderwort *Utricularia chrysantha*
FAMILY Lentibulariaceae
A tiny herb which grows on damp flats beside receding swamps or in still shallow water. On the roots are tiny bladders which act as box traps: when a mosquito lava or other small aquatic creature touches a triggering hair the evacuated bladder opens, the prey is swept in with the rush of water, and is slowly digested. Of Australia's 40 or more bladderworts more than half are in the tropics. Flowering time is May to Aug.

Small-Leaved Fringe Myrtle
Calytrix microphyl
FAMILY Myrtaceae
The flowers are usually pink, turning violet before finally fading to white. Their shape resembles others of the genus, with distinctive long fine points to the sepals. This species is named for its extremely fine foliage, leaves being barely 2 to 3 mm long. It occurs as a larg shrub or small tree on stony areas of tropical NT and the Kimberleys. Flowering time is Mar. to Nov.

Dillenia alata
FAMILY Dilleniaceae
A north-east Qld rainforest tree with flowers similar to those of the well-known genus *Hibbertia*, to which it is closely related. The flowers are large and showy, the leaves large, glossy dark green. Flowering time is summer to autumn.

Cocky Apple *Planchonia careya*
FAMILY Lecythidaceae
A widely distributed tree around coastal tropical Australia from north-east Qld to NT. The pink filamentous flowers are quite large and showy, but delicate, stamens falling easily. Leaves are up to 4 in. long, spathulate to obovate in shape, with slightly crenate margins. Flowering time is the dry season, winter to spring.

King Orchid *Dendrobium speciosum* var. *hillii*
FAMILY Orchidaceae
Growing almost exclusively on giant rainfores trees from northern NSW to northern Qld, th huge clumps of bright yellow flowers may be seen a hundred feet or more above the ground This variety has pseudobulbs up to 3 ft long, and numerous long pendant racemes. Flowerin time is Aug. to Oct.

Native Passionfruit *Passiflora herbertiana*
FAMILY Passifloraceae
A climbing plant of the coastal and mountain
rainforests of Qld and north-east NSW. Leaves
are large, 3-lobed; flower colour variable,
reddish-yellow or greenish. Fruits are green,
oval, resembling those of the cultivated passionfruit. Flowering time is Sept. to Nov.

Wild Cotton *Cochlospermum gregori*
FAMILY Cochlospermaceae
This small tree's common name is due to the
seed capsules's filling of soft downy cotton-like
hairs. As it is almost leafless during the dry
season the many large bright yellow buttercup-
like flowers are conspicuous. It occurs in tropical
woodlands, 'top end' of NT, Arnhem Land,
Gulf of Carpentaria, Cape York. Flowering time
is May to Sept.

Stately Orchid *Dendrobium superbiens*
FAMILY Orchidaceae
This epiphytic orchid is usually found on trees,
but also on moist shaded boulders in places
where it is especially common in the trees. Its
flowers are in long racemes, and are large with
undulate petals and sepals. Native to north-east
Qld and the northern islands. A long flowering
period.

Pink Rock Orchid *Dendrobium kingianum*
FAMILY Orchidaceae
The flower colour varies from white to deep
pink. This leafy spreading plant forms
extensive low clumps across mossy boulders,
and bears numerous short flower racemes. It
occurs in sclerophyll forests of coastal Qld and
north-east NSW. Flowering time is Aug. to Oct.

Tree Spider Orchid *Dendrobium tetragonum*
FAMILY Orchidaceae
A strange epiphytic orchid which has long,
four-angled stems narrowest at their base.
Flowers are small, with long pointed segments,
yellow-green with red-brown markings, faintly
fragrant and borne in clusters at stem tips or
from joints. This orchid grows on tree trunks
in coastal and mountain areas of Qld and
northern NSW. Flowering time is spring and
summer.

Ironbark or **White Feather Orchid**
Dendrobium aemulu
FAMILY Orchidaceae
This epiphytic orchid may be found growing
in small clumps on rainforest trees in NSW an
Qld. It has fine, almost feathery flowers in
short racemes, and slender pseudobulbs.

Silky Oak *Grevillea robusta* ▶
FAMILY Proteaceae
A tall erect tree with light-green foliage of
much-divided, pinnate leaves. The branched
inflorescences are made up of several long
racemes of orange-yellow flowers, while the
fruit is a ¾-in. boat-shaped follicle containing
winged seeds. It is native to the rainforests of
north-east NSW and south-east Qld but is
widely grown as an ornamental tree.
Flowering time is Oct. to Dec.

Native Rosella *Hibiscus heterophyllus*
FAMILY Malvaceae
A tall rather prickly shrub or small tree with
variable leaves, these being cordate to
lanceolate, stiff, glabrous, often three-lobed and
usually shortly toothed along the margins. The
flowers unfold within an hour or so in the warm
morning sunlight, crimson buds expanding,

petals unfolding to show pink then white
streaks that grow until it is an almost-white
flower veined with crimson and with crimson-
purple centre. Flowering time is spring and
summer.

Flame Tree *Brachychiton acerifolium* ▶
FAMILY Sterculiaceae
A medium to large tree occurring in coastal
rainforests northwards, from Illawarra (NSW)
into Qld. Its numerous waxy scarlet bells hang
in long panicles from bare branches, the leaves
being dropped when the tree is in full bloom.
Leaves vary from palmately lobed on young
trees, to entire, and dark glossy green. Seeds
form in large woody boat-shaped capsules.
Flowering time is Oct. to Mar.

Orange Blossom Orchid *Sarcochilus falcatus*
FAMILY Orchidaceae
The large flowers, 1 in. or more in diameter,
hanging in multiple racemes, are highly
perfumed in the warmth of the morning sun.
It is an epiphytic species, native to north-eastern
NSW and Qld. Flowering time is Sept. to Jan.

Brewster's Cassia *Cassia brewsteri* ▶
FAMILY Caesalpiniaceae
A compact, bush tree up to 40 ft high, with
lush foliage of glossy, pinnately-divided leaves.
The yellow flowers hang in profusion on
clusters of long slender racemes. A highly
ornamental species, native to Qld rainforests.
Flowering time is Oct. to Dec.

Pimelia Poppy or **Red-Hot Poker**
Pimelea haematostachya
FAMILY Thymelaeaceae
A spectacular species, with large heads of blood-
red flowers at the tips of stems several feet tall.
It grows on clay soils and appears to be
confined to the area drained by the tributaries
of the Fitzroy and Burdekin rivers, Qld.
Flowering time is Sept. to Nov. A similar
species, *P. decora*, has broader leaves and occurs
on heavy clays of north-west Qld.

Phaius tankervilliae
FAMILY Orchidaceae
A terrestrial orchid with abundant large, showy
flowers, borne in terminal racemes at the tips of
long stems rising to 6 ft above ground. The
labellum is rolled into a distinctive trumpet-
shaped tube, encircling the column. Leaves are
large, fleshy, broad-lanceolate and fluted.
Occurs in coastal swamps and occasionally
moist hillsides from northern NSW to north
Qld and through Indonesia, Burma, India and
China. Flowering time is Sept. to Nov.

Cotton Tree *Cochlospermum heteroneurum*
FAMILY Cochlospermaceae
Along the rough limestone ridges of the Napier
and Oscar ranges, and further northwards in
the rugged King Leopolds, this *Cochlospermum*
is a conspicuous feature of the dry-season
Kimberley landscape. Unlike the very similar
Cochlospermum gregorii of the NT, it has some
leaves at time of flowering which is May to
Sept.

The South-West Vegetation Province of Western Australia lies approximately to the west and south of a line between Shark Bay and Israelite Bay. The boundary is rather irregular, with extensions on both sides by the South-West and Eremaean Provinces, *see* maps page 120. Within the Province there is a mixture of forest, woodland, coastal scrub, sandheaths, swamps and salt flats. The vegetation differs from that of the Eremaea chiefly in the predominance of the families Myrtaceae, Proteaceae, Papilionaceae Tribe Podalyriae and Epacridaceae.

Within the Province there are over 3,000 species of which some 75 percent are endemic. However, most of the families and genera occur in northern or eastern Australia, indicating that they had spread widely over the continent before the development of the arid desert barrier and the Nullarbor Plain which effectively stopped migration to and from the South-West. The endemic families are few and small, and include the Pitcher Plant *Cephalotus* and a curious plant called *Emblingia* whose affinities with other plants still puzzle botanists. Endemic genera include the Parrot Bushes, *Dryandra*, the bottlebrushes, *Calothamnus* and *Eremaea*, the heaths, *Andersonia*, the flame peas, *Chorizema*, orchids such as the Hammer Orchids, *Drakaea*, and the kangaroo paws, *Anigozanthos*. Many other genera are most highly developed here, having only a few species outside the State. These include the featherflowers, *Verticordia*, the poison peas, *Gastrolobium*, the trigger-plants, *Stylidium*, and the native foxgloves, *Pityrodia*.

The principal factors affecting the distribution of plants in the South-West are climate and soil. Altitude has little effect, as the region consists chiefly of a large gently undulating plateau with a narrow coastal plain. Only a few high hills such as the Stirling Range and the Barrens to the east have any plants which are possibly restricted by altitude. On the other hand, rainfall is a limiting factor for many species, ranging from over 60″ in the south-western corner to less than 10″ inland where it is also less reliable. The Karri forest, for example, requires over 40″ of rain and is restricted to the wetter parts. It is the only formation here with relatively soft-leaved shrubs forming the understorey. The Jarrah forest tolerates up to 50″ or more, but is limited at its outer boundary by about the 30″ isohyet; an interesting point is the occurrence of a few outliers which indicate that jarrah was more widespread in wetter times. In the drier areas are various types of woodland, and large tracts of scrub which contain the richest development of our flora.

Throughout the Province soil is a dominant influence on plant distribution. In any one area, the vegetation types clearly follow the

PART 5 SOUTH-WEST

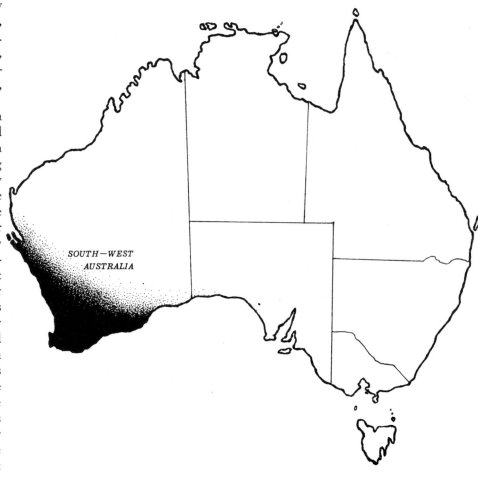

SOUTH—WEST
AUSTRALIA

distribution of soil types. For example, in the central and south-eastern wheatbelt, there is salmon gum woodland on deep red loam, jam savannah on granitic loam, wandoo woodland on clay and sandheath on shallow sandy clay overlying laterite; yet all these may share approximately the same climate. It is noteworthy that towards and beyond the boundary of the South-West Province the rainfall is less than 10″ and irregular, yet Eucalyptus trees may grow to over 80 feet tall.

An interesting feature is the outcropping of granite as monadnocks which are scattered throughout the south-west. These usually have large bare or lichen-covered rock expanses which allow rainwater to run off and increase the ground-water in the immediate vicinity. The soil, being derived from the granite, also differs from that away from the rock, and these two factors combine to support a different vegetation. Many plants are entirely restricted to these outcrops, e.g. the red or white flowered *Kunzea pulchella*. Other species from wetter areas can survive due to the increased run-off, e.g. *Hypocalymma angustifolium*, the White Myrtle. Shallow soil pockets on the rocks are often water-logged in winter and baked dry in summer. They carry a myriad of plants, mostly very small, and one can spend hours hunting all the species in a small area. Two intriguing species here are the Pincushion Plant, *Borya nitida*, and the Elbow Orchid, *Spiculaea ciliata*, which are peculiarly adapted to such an extreme habitat. These granite outcrops are virtually islands in the surrounding countryside, and it is interesting to study and speculate on the effect of such isolation on the evolution of their flora and fauna.

Environmental effects on the flora are many and are largely aimed at ensuring their survival during the long, hot, dry summer. To prevent dessication of the vegetative parts, features have developed such as leaf reduction or loss, layers of various types of scales or hairs and viscid excretions on leaves and stems. A thick corky layer around stems assists some species to avoid damage when the soil is hot. Many plants have very small leaves, often with tightly rolled margins, while others have long, needle-like leaves held vertically to escape the direct impact of solar radiation. Some plants such as wattles have the leaves replaced by expanded leaf-stalks which assume the functions of leaves. Often there is a double system of roots, some penetrating deeply to utilise ground water, others lying just below the surface where they can take advantage of heavy dew or brief summer showers. Many small plants such as orchids, lilies and everlastings, avoid rather than endure the dry season by means of dormant tubers, rhizomes, seeds, etc. There are also many internal and physiological adaptions which assist plants to survive the summer.

A striking development among the flora is an inflorescence of numerous flowers, individually small but often produced in a mass which resembles a large single flower. The feather flowers, *Verticordia*, and *Banksia* and *Dryandra* are outstanding examples. A misleading one is the Swamp Daisy, *Actinodium*, which is not a true daisy but a myrtle; the outer 'ray' flowers are sterile, while the short inner ones are fertile. The brilliance and range of colour are also striking. Some genera have developed a whole range, e.g. *Lechenaultia*, with shades of red, orange, yellow, green, blue, mauve and white. Bizarre combinations occur, such as the common Kangaroo Paw with a red stem and green flowers, and the pea flower *Gompholobium venustum* which is red and blue. When one or several species are in full flower they appear to dominate an area but a visit at another time may reveal other species making a similar display while the previous plants have finished flowering and become inconspicuous again. It is the production of such masses of flowers which gives the South-Western bushland its garden appearance.

To those familiar with the bush it is clear that fire is an important factor in its survival. It is essential that we learn how to use it in the management of national parks and reserves. A fire-devastated area should not be regarded as a destroyed one: it is really the beginning of a new cycle in its growth. An immediate result of fire is the release of seeds from many plants such as Banksia, Eucalyptus, Casuarina, etc. In some cases only the death of the stems is needed to make the fruits open, but in others fire is essential. The latter may die out completely if there is never a fire. Many other plants have seeds which remain dormant in the soil until stimulated by a fire to germinate. These include ephemerals as well as short-lived shrubs such as certain species of smokebush. They often flower profusely, so that there is a

Babe-in-a-Cradle *Epiblema grandiflorum*
Colour: deep violet-blue. Occurrence: swampy flats, south-west of W.A. Flowering: Nov. to Mar.

flush of flowers a few years after a fire, followed by a general tailing off as these plants die and are overtaken by long-lived species. A curious feature of many wildflowers is that while they produce abundant flowers, only a small proportion of these set viable seed. In some cases this is offset by the development of a perennial stock which regenerates after fire, so that seed is not necessary for survival. However, in other cases where seed is essential, the thousands of apparently good fruit set may contain few viable seed.

There are also many species which will flower only in the first year after a bushfire e.g. two of the Rattlebeak Orchids, *Lyperanthus nigricans* and *L. forrestii*, and certain species of sundew (*Drosera*). Others which flower occasion-

Scented Boronia *Boronia megastigma*
FAMILY Rutaceae
Colour: yellow inside; red outside, becoming purple-brown on older flowers.
Occurrence: sandy swamps near south coast of WA. Flowering: Aug. to Sept.

Rattle-Beak Orchid *Lyperanthus serratus*
FAMILY Orchidaceae
Colour: yellow-green with dark crimson streaks. Occurrence: south coast of WA. Flowering: Sept. to Oct.

Leafless Fringe-Lily *Thysanotus sparteus*
FAMILY Liliaceae
Colour: blue-violet. Occurrence: widespread through southern WA. Flowering: Dec. to Mar.

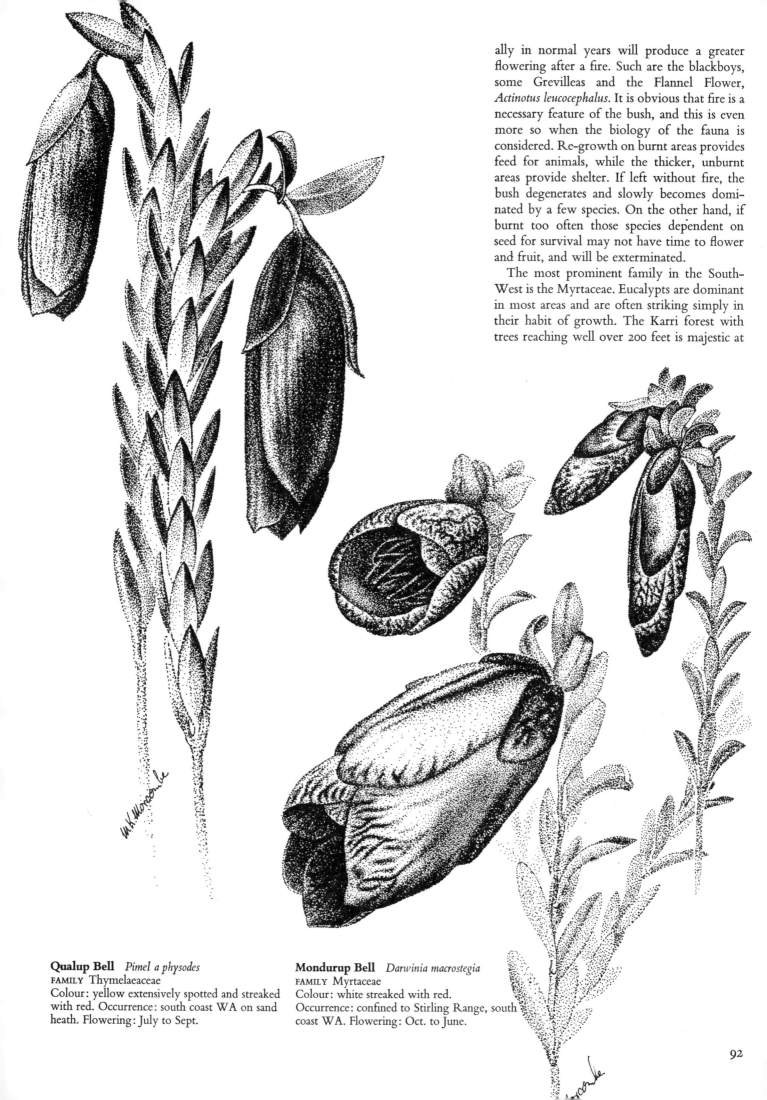

ally in normal years will produce a greater flowering after a fire. Such are the blackboys, some Grevilleas and the Flannel Flower, *Actinotus leucocephalus*. It is obvious that fire is a necessary feature of the bush, and this is even more so when the biology of the fauna is considered. Re-growth on burnt areas provides feed for animals, while the thicker, unburnt areas provide shelter. If left without fire, the bush degenerates and slowly becomes dominated by a few species. On the other hand, if burnt too often those species dependent on seed for survival may not have time to flower and fruit, and will be exterminated.

The most prominent family in the South-West is the Myrtaceae. Eucalypts are dominant in most areas and are often striking simply in their habit of growth. The Karri forest with trees reaching well over 200 feet is majestic at

Qualup Bell *Pimel a physodes*
FAMILY Thymelaeaceae
Colour: yellow extensively spotted and streaked with red. Occurrence: south coast WA on sand heath. Flowering: July to Sept.

Mondurup Bell *Darwinia macrostegia*
FAMILY Myrtaceae
Colour: white streaked with red.
Occurrence: confined to Stirling Range, south coast WA. Flowering: Oct. to June.

92

any time of the year. At the other extreme are mallees which flower when only two or three feet tall. An unusual form is the Weeping Gum, *Eucalyptus sepulcralis*, a small slender mallee with graceful pendulous branches. Another contrast is the Mottlecah, *E. macrocarpa*, whose large white leaves never pass beyond the juvenile stage; most Eucalypts develop the 'normal' gum leaf after the seedling stage. The Mottlecah also has the largest Eucalypt flower, some three or four inches across. Brightly coloured flowers—red, pink, yellow, etc.—are more common among the south-western gums than elsewhere. The bark may also be attractive, as in the Salmon Gum, Powder-bark Wandoo and the White Mallee whose bark turns deep red in the autumn. In many myrtles a feature of the flowers is the conspicuous development of the stamens, while the petals remain small. The bottlebrushes—*Beaufortia*, *Callistemon*, *Melaleuca*, etc.—are the best examples. On the other hand in the featherflowers, *Verticordia*, the feathery calyx usually envelops the whole flower. The production of masses of brightly coloured flowers by these plants is a feature of the bushland.

The Banksia family with about 500 species is represented almost throughout the Province, being especially well-developed on sandheaths. Four genera are endemic—*Dryandra*, *Franklandia*, *Stirlingia* and *Synaphea*, but others such as *Banksia* and *Hakea* have far more species here than elsewhere. Although their often prickly leaves add to the discomfort of the Australian bush, their extraordinary range of forms, e.g. in leaf shape and flower colour, add much to its unique character, while the oddly shaped fruits are also intriguing. Among many remarkable species one of the most unusual is the Lantern Hakea, *H. victoriae*, the only native plant in the State with variegated leaves. These change from cream to orange-red with age and the plants often stand prominently above the scrub in which they grow. The prostrate species of *Banksia* are curious too, their stems and flower spikes resting on the surface of the soil. Another odd habit is seen in several *Grevillea* species in which the flowers are borne on long almost leafless canes which arch above the foliage. Such are *G. leucopteris* and *G. petrophiloides*. The smoke bushes, *Conospermum*, are also varied. In contrast to the well-known woolly-flowered species, some have smooth, white flowers while others are blue, a rare colour in this family. Yet another species has large cream bracts enclosing small flowers and providing the most conspicuous feature of the inflorescence.

The family Fabaceae, the legumes, includes the wattles and pea flowers. The wattles are ubiquitous, as they are throughout Australia, with well over 100 species in the South-West.

They mostly have phyllodes (expanded leaf stalks) in place of true leaves, while a few such as *Acacia diptera* have only flattened stems. Sometimes they are dominant trees as in the case of *A. acuminata*, the Raspberry-jam tree and *A. microbotrya*, the Manna Wattle, in parts of the wheatbelt. More often they are shrubs mixed with other plants but giving a bright display when they flower, usually in winter or spring. Near Perth the Prickly Moses, *A. pulchella*, gives hillsides a golden aspect in July and August, while further south the Karri Wattle, *A. pentadenia*, is prominent in October. Both these have true pinnate leaves.

The pea flowers are also mostly shrubs, though a few are annual and some are strong climbers, especially *Kennedia* and *Hardenbergia*. Orange, red and yellow are the common colours, but pink, purple and even black and blue occur. Some of the most brilliant are the flame peas, *Chorizema*, which display their red, pink and orange flowers in the spring. They are especially common in south coastal districts. Also on the south coast grows *Kennedia nigricans*, a vigorous climber with striking black and yellow flowers. This family includes a number of toxic plants which have caused stock losses ever since the early settlers drove their sheep and cattle over the hills in the 1830s. A curious growth form is seen in *Brachysema daviesioides* which inhabits areas between Wubin and Coolgardie. It has intricately divided leafless branchlets tipped with spines, and the deep red flowers lie on the soil in a ring around the plant. Another oddity is *Daviesia epiphylla*. This too is leafless, having flattened whitish stems resembling staghorns in shape, and red flowers which arise from the flat surface of the stems. It grows to the north of Badgingarra.

The heath family, *Epacridaceae*, is represented by some fifteen genera and more than 150 species. They are mostly shrubs with very small leaves and small tubular flowers, often white but sometimes pink or red. In a few *Andersonia* species there is a pink calyx and a bright blue corolla. In forests of the lower South-West occurs the Tassel Flower, *Leucopogon verticillatus*, which has unusually large leaves in widely-spaced whorls, the flowers being small and dull pink. Many heaths add colour to the bush in winter when few other plants are flowering.

The family *Verbenaceae* includes the attractive Lambs' Tails and Native Foxgloves which have

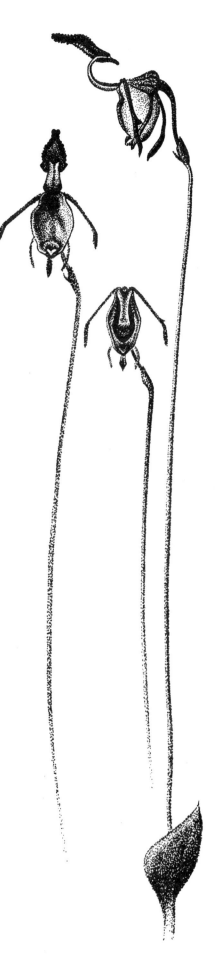

Flying Ducks *Caleana nigrita*
FAMILY Orchidaceae
Colour: purple-brown. Occurrence: south-west Jarrah and Karri forests. Flowering: Oct.

Clubbed Spider Orchid *Caladenia longiclavata*
FAMILY Orchidaceae
Colour: yellow with red stripes, and maroon
tip to labellum. Occurrence: extreme south-west
of WA. Flowering: Oct. to Dec.

a dense covering of woolly hairs. The flowers, arranged in spikes or loose panicles, are also almost enveloped in white or yellow hairs. In *Lachnostachys*, *Newcastelia* and *Dicrastylis* the petals are very small and hidden, only the stamens protruding from the 'wool'. *Pityrodia* has flowers like a small foxglove, pink, mauve, orange or white in colour, while in the very similar *Hemiphora* of the eastern Goldfields the whole inflorescence is of a deep wine-red colour.

The triggerplants, *Stylidium*, always attract attention to their sensitive column. This bears both anthers and stigma which mature at different times to ensure cross-pollination. An insect visiting the flower triggers the column which flicks over to deposit pollen on the insect or to collect pollen on the stigma if another flower has already been visited. Although they are small plants the flowers are brightly coloured and often form dense colonies, especially on sandy flats, swamps or granite outcrops. About 100 species occur in the South-West.

A plant which gives the Australian bush some of its unique character is the blackboy, *Xanthorrhoea*. Far from being a primitive plant these are considered to be highly developed members of the lily family. Fire is necessary to remove the old leaves and give them the black trunks, while it also stimulates flowering. The Black Gin, *Kingia*, with drumstick-like flower heads is a close ally. Another impressive species is the Blue Tinsel Lily, a stiff perennial with pungent leaves and papery flowers of an iridescent blue or purple; the stamens turn orange or red as they mature. Of more transient beauty are the fringed lilies, *Thysanotus*, whose elegantly fringed purple flowers open only for a morning. A curious species of the Stirling Range and South coast is the Hooded Lily, *Johnsonia*, whose papery white or pink bracts conceal the tiny flowers.

Allied to the lilies are the Kangaroo Paws, *Anigozanthos* and *Macropidia*, which include the State's floral emblem. The striking colours red, orange, yellow, green and black—are intensified by a dense covering of velvety hairs on the flowers. Of more lowly stature is the Red Bugle, *Blancoa*, with brick-red bell-like flowers which appear among the grass-like leaves in mid-winter. The Cotton-Heads, *Conostylis*, are of similar habit but have woolly heads of yellow or white flowers. This whole group is restricted to the South-West.

The orchids of Western Australia are mostly restricted to the South-West Province. About three-quarters of the 150 species are endemic, including four genera. These are *Elythranthera*, the Enamelled Orchids with shining flowers of pink or purple; *Drakaea*, the Hammer Orchids so named from their curious shape; *Epiblema*, a tall swamp-loving species with spotted mauve flowers; and the extraordinary Underground Orchid, *Rhizanthella*, which lives entirely below the soil surface. Better known are the spider orchids, *Caladenia*, with a wide range of flower size and colour as is shown in their common names—White Spider Orchid, Blue China Orchid, Yellow Orchid, Pink Fairies, etc. The Sun Orchids, *Thelymitra*, are unusual in the family in having almost regular flowers. These open only in sunny weather, and again show a wide range of colours. Blue is a common colour in this genus. The Leek Orchids, *Prasophyllum*, have about 18 species here, including one of the tallest terrestrial orchids in Australia, *P. elatum*, which grows to 6 feet tall. However, these orchids have small, relatively drab flowers. More attractive are the Donkey Orchids, *Diuris*, with wallflower-coloured flowers. Among the curious orchids are the Rattlebeaks, *Lyperanthus nigricans*, which turn completely black on drying; the Beard Orchid, *Calochilus*, with a densely bushy lip, and the Slipper Orchid, *Cryptostylis*, which uses sexual attraction to lure the pollinating insects. The Greenhoods, *Pterostylis*, also have some odd shapes among their striped green or brown flowers, and have another intriguing feature in the sensitive lip which traps visiting insects and forces them to escape past the stigma and anther, thus ensuring cross-pollination.

It is impossible to adequately summarize this flora, and it can only be properly appreciated when seen in its natural condition. Its unique features are always a surprise and fascination to the observer, whether local or visiting from other states or overseas. To hear a visiting botanist exclaim, often with envy, over our plants is to realise even more strongly what an invaluable asset they are to science and to the tourist industry. Once the vegetation is unduly disturbed or destroyed, it is impossible to restore it, and it is imperative to retain large areas as reserves and national parks and to preserve them by correct management. Some large parks are already established, and management techniques are being developed, but this is only a beginning. More reserves are needed so that adequate representative samples of all flora and fauna types will be preserved. There is no doubt that future generations will appreciate the existence of these areas for recreation and scientific study.

A. S. George,
Botanist,
Western Australian Herbarium,
Department of Agriculture,
South Perth, W.A.

Alex George, B.A., was born in Fremantle, Western Australia, in 1939, and graduated in Arts from the University of Western Australia in 1963. He has been on the staff of the Western Australian Herbarium since 1959, and in 1968 was Australian Botanical Liaison Officer at the Royal Botanic Gardens, Kew, England. His main interest is the study of the Western Australian flora, and especially the families Orchidaceae and Proteaceae. He has written a number of papers in connection with these studies and was co-author with H. E. Foote of the booklet Orchids of Western Australia.

Jug Orchid *Pterostylis recurva*
FAMILY
Colour: deep green with white translucent stripes. Occurrence: southern parts of WA. Flowering: Aug. to Sept.

95

NATIONAL PARKS AND WILDFLOWER RESERVES

ALBANY COASTLINE NATIONAL PARK RESERVE (A24258, A27107) (WA)
Several miles SW of Albany.

Coastal hills and cliffs, scenic features include The Gap, Blowhole, Natural Bridge. The stunted, windswept coastal vegetation has many wildflowers: *Banksia grandis*, Christmas Tree (*Nuytsia*), and *Banksia attenuata*.

BEEDELUP NATIONAL PARK (WA)
Extreme SW, about 10 m. W of Pemberton.

Hilly, with wet-sclerophyll forest including tall Karri; many wildflowers, best seen Sept. to Oct.

BIG BROOK NATIONAL PARK (WA)
Extreme SW, next to Pemberton.

Karri forests with huge trees; lush undergrowth, good wildflower displays in spring months.

CAPE ARID NATIONAL PARK (WA)
S coast, about 100 m. E of Esperance.

Granite headlands, sandplains. Area of great botanical importance because it contains the flora first examined by botanist Robert Brown, who accompanied Matthew Flinders on voyage of exploration in 1801.

DRYANDRA STATE FOREST (WA)
In SW, a few miles from Narrogin.

An extremely important sanctuary for Mallee Fowl and Numbat, this forest contains a number of species of *Dryandra*, a genus entirely confined to WA.

FITZGERALD RIVER FLORA AND FAUNA RESERVE (WA)
S coast, about 140 m. E of Albany, 150 m. W of Esperance.

Coastal ranges and extensive sandplains. Reserve was established because of exceptional richness of flora (25 endemic species); Sept. to April.

JOHN FORREST NATIONAL PARK (WA)
On edge of Darling Range escarpment overlooking Perth; 16 m. E of Perth, on Gt Eastern Hwy.

Undulating hills, valleys, Jarrah forest, undergrowth rich in flowering plants: Red-and-green Kangaroo-paws, Swan River Myrtle, Blue Leschenaultia, Hovea, Pink Calytrix. Popular with visitors to Perth in winter–spring. This park has now been pegged for mining claims.

KALBARRI NATIONAL PARK (WA)
On coast 415 m. (by road) N of Perth, at mouth of Murchison R.

Rich sandplain flora, with magnificent flowering trees and shrubs throughout the year, particularly early spring to summer. Species include *Verticordia grandiflora*, *Banksia ashbyi*, *B. sceptrum*, *Grevillea leucopteris*, *Lechenaultia hirsuta*, *Melaleuca steedmanii* and *Grevillea petrophiloides*.

NAMBUNG NATIONAL PARK (WA)
Near W coast, about 120 m. N of Perth via Jurien Bay; access via sandy track.

Coastal limestone country, sandplains, heathland with scattered banksias, stunted gums, mallee thickets. Wildflowers spring and summer; scenic 'Pinnacles'.

NEERABUP NATIONAL PARK (WA)
Near W coast, about 22 m. N of Perth, along W side of Perth–Yanchep road.

Open forest with banksia and lower scrub undergrowth, many wildflowers Aug. to Nov.: *Banksia menziesi*, Kangaroo-paws, *Hardenbergia* vines.

PORONGORUP RANGE NATIONAL PARK (WA)
Near S coast, 25 m. N of main regional port of Albany.

High hills, bare granite domes, boulders, Karri forest on the lower slopes, with flowering trees and creepers such as *Banksia grandis*, and *Clematis*.

SOUTH-WEST CAVES (YALLINGUP AND MARGARET RIVER) (WA)
A number of small reserves at extreme SW of State via Bunbury, Busselton.

Coastal limestone region (in which at least 120 very beautiful caves have been discovered) with magnificent Karri trees, lush undergrowth, wildflowers Sept. to Oct. or Nov. (Pegged for mining leases.)

STIRLING RANGES NATIONAL PARK (WA)
Near S coast, about 55 m. N of Albany via Porongorups, or 210 m. S of Perth.

Very steep, jagged peaks of sedimentary rock, rising above flat plains; dry sclerophyll forests and low dense scrub. Magnificent scenery and many wildflowers, including some (*Darwinia macrostegia*, *D. leistyla*, *D. meeboldii*), found nowhere else; also *Banksia coccinea*, *Dryandra formosa*, *Eucalyptus preissiana*.

TWO PEOPLE BAY FLORA AND FAUNA RESERVE (WA)
S coast, about 15 m. E of Albany.

High coastal granite hills, coastal lakes, thickets of mallee, banksia, peppermint. Principally set aside for the Noisy Scrub Bird, but also has numerous flowering shrubs, particularly *Banksias*.

WALPOLE–NORNALUP NATIONAL PARK (WA)
S coast, 70 m. W of Albany.

Karri forest, coastal hills with sandplain. Trees include Karri, Red Tingle, Jarrah, Marri, *Casuarina*, *Banksia*, with undergrowth of Karri Wattle, Crowea, Tree Kangaroo-paw (*Anigosanthos viridis*), and orchids such as Babe-in-Cradle (*Epiblema*) and Potato Orchid (*Gastrodia sesamoides*).

WALYUNGA NATIONAL PARK (WA)
N of Perth on E side of Gt Northern Hwy between 22 and 23-mile posts.

Attractive upper reaches of Swan R., with wildflowers typical of Darling Range, Blue Leschenaultia, Hovea, Red-and-green Kangaroo-paw, various *Grevillea* shrubs. (Recently partly pegged for mining.)

WARREN NATIONAL PARK (WA)
Extreme SW corner, near Pemberton, 211 m. S of Perth.

Undulating hills with tall Karri trees (*Eucalyptus diversicolor*) reaching to 250 ft, lush undergrowth with wildflowers Sept. to Oct.

YANCHEP NATIONAL PARK (WA)
32 m. N of Perth via Wanneroo Rd.

Coastal limestone and sandy plains, Tuart forest, Marri gums, dense undergrowth with many wildflowers (also limestone caves).

YALGORUP NATIONAL PARK (WA)
SW, about 80 m. S of Perth on W side of Old Coast Road between Mandurah and Bunbury.

Sandy coastal country, dunes with heaths, Tuart forest, with *Banksia* and *Acacia* understorey.

Crimson Swamp Banksia *Banksia occidentalis*
FAMILY Proteaceae
The long cylindrical flower spikes when small are
bright light green, incised with the lines of
diagonal rows of developing flowers; later,
reaching a length of near 12 in., they carry rows
of looped glossy red styles, which spring open
from the top of the spike downwards. The
leaves are long, narrow-linear, with denticulate
margins towards their tips. This shrub occurs
along the south coast of WA. Flowering
time is Jan. to Feb. or Mar.

Morrison *Verticordia nitens*
FAMILY Myrtaceae
The single straight stem of the mature plant
rises leafless and without branching to
3-6 ft. high, then branches repeatedly near the
top to support an umbrella-shaped crown of
foliage up to 1 ft. diameter. During November
and December this crown is covered with tiny
feathery flowers; each year a new crown of
foliage, then of flowers, is added an inch or so
above the old.

Fuchsia Grevillea *Grevillea bipinnatifida*
FAMILY Proteaceae
This low, sometimes almost procumbent shrub
has extremely attractive foliage. The leaves are
large and pinnately divided into wide, pointed
lobes, which themselves are again similarly
divided, resulting in a most intricate leaf pattern.
The flowers, borne on long pendant racemes,
are dusky orange-red. This grevillea occurs on
gravel and granite soils of the Darling Range
near Perth, flowering June to Dec.

Pimelea suaveolens
FAMILY Thymelaeaceae
A widely-dispersed species occurring in
numerous forms on mid-west coast, south-west
and southern inland WA. The flowers of this
low, slender-stemmed shrub are heads of many
small flowers, each a fine tube, with 4 spreading
lobes surrounding its opening; there are 2
stamens, and petals are absent. Around the head
is an involucre of yellow-green bracts.
Flowering time is June to Nov.

Showy Dryandra *Dryandra formosa* ◀
FAMILY Proteaceae
A tall shrub on the Stirling Ranges, or more
stunted on Albany coastal hills, it carries a
profusion of large, deep-golden flower heads,
borne on the tips of branches, and having a
golden-metallic sheen. Leaves are green above,
white beneath, long, narrow (less than ¼ in.),
and finely but deeply serrated. Flowering time
is Sept. to Nov.

Dryandra speciosa
FAMILY Proteaceae
Grows as a dense shrub 3 to 15 ft tall, with
flower-heads hanging downwards, half-hidden
beneath the leafy apex of the supporting
branchlet. The numerous
bracts of *Dryandra speciosa* are exceptionally long
(up to 2 in.), narrow, with densely hairy
margins; outer bracts are fine and hair-like, and
continue as short rigid scales onto the supporting
branchlet. Inside this cup-like involucre of
bracts is a clustered mass of flowers. Each
individual flower has a stiff rod-like orange-
yellow perianth tube. Each carries 4 stamens,
one fused to each segment of the perianth.
Massed together, the tips of perianth-limbs and
the golden anthers form the colourful centre of
a *Dryandra* flower head. This species grows on
sand heaths of inland south-west WA (Avon
district). Flowers May to Sept.

Scarlet Leschenaultia *Lechenaultia hirsuta*
FAMILY Goodeniaceae
One of the most brilliantly coloured of WA's
20 leschenaultias. This wiry little shrub, usually
less than 18 in. tall, has sparse foliage; its leaves
and stems are glandular-hairy. Occurs on
central-west coastal sandplains (Irwin district).
May be propagated by seed, cuttings, or division
of existing plants. Flowers Sept. to Jan.

Giant Banksia *Banksia grandis* ▶
FAMILY Proteaceae
Giant cylindrical flower spikes, 12 to 15 in. long
and wide, foot-long, saw-toothed leaves make
this a decorative species. From north of Perth
to the extreme south-west it grows as an
understorey tree (reaching 40 ft) beneath tall
eucalypts of the jarrah and karri forests. But as
shown here, on the windswept granite headlands of the south coast it remains a stunted
shrub. Flowering time is Oct. to Feb.

Protea-Like Dryandra *Dryandra proteoides*
FAMILY Proteaceae
A low, prickly, densely-foliaged shrub, with
foliage and flowers similar, yet distinct from,
those of *D. runcinata*. In some localities the two
species grow intermingled. Leaves are long,
thin, pinnatifid, with sinus margin almost
parallel to midrib. Flower heads are large,
enclosed in bronzed bracts. Grows in
dense low thickets on gravelly-lateritic hills
south-west WA. Flowers June to Sept.

Dryandra stuposa
FAMILY Proteaceae
A shrub 6 to 8 ft high. Leaves long, thin,
deeply pinnatifid, divided almost in to the
midrib, lobes triangular, widely spaced. Flower
heads are several inches in diameter, yellow to
bronzed-golden. Grows in dense low thickets
on rocky or gravelly lateritic hilltops, inland
south-west WA (Dale and Stirling districts).
Flowering time is June to Jan.

Rose Cone-Bush *Isopogon dubius*
FAMILY Proteaceae
A low, dense shrub rarely exceeding 18 in. high
with harsh prickly foliage; leaves flat, ternately
divided; large flower heads. *Isopogon* is distinguished from a similar genus *Petrophile* by its
deciduous seed-cone scales, which soon fall to
leave a smooth cone. The cones of *Petrophile*
remain permanently covered by scales. Occurs
on clay soils of the Darling Range (near Perth).
Flowering time is Aug. to Oct.

Grevillea wilsonii
FAMILY Proteaceae
This low prickly species is a common undershrub
of the Darling Ranges near Perth, and through
the forested south-west of WA. The brilliant
scarlet, hard, glossy flowers are borne on short
racemes among foliage of much-divided,
needle-like leaves. It attracts many honeyeaters
(such as Western Spinebills) which are its
pollinators. Flowering time is Sept. to Nov.

Round-Fruited Banksia *Banksia sphaerocarpa*
FAMILY Proteaceae
Widespread and variable small shrub occurring
from Geraldton (west coast) to Bremer Bay
(south coast) on sandplains and on lateritic
ranges. Leaves are narrow-linear, with two
grooves along the undersurface. Flowers form
spherical heads up to 4 in. diameter, yellow,
bronzed or violet (variety, or species, *violacea*).
Style ends remain hooked after flowers have
opened. Flowers Oct. to Jan.

Firewood Banksia *Banksia menziesi*
FAMILY Proteaceae
A small to medium sized, spreading, rough-
barked tree to 30 ft. Leaves are long, with
dentate margins, grey-green beneath and dark
glossy green above. Flower spikes are usually
pink, changing to orange as the flower opens,
but in some areas occasional yellow-flowered
trees may be seen. This is a common banksia
around Perth and along the western coastal
plain of WA. Flowering time is May to Sept.

A Pink Boronia *Boronia viminea* ▶
FAMILY Rutaceae
One of WA's 46 species of boronia, this is a
slender upright shrub of sandy west and south-
coastal plains. Boronia leaves contain oil glands,
and give off a strongly aromatic perfume when
crushed. Flowers of the genus have a 4-lobed
calyx, 4 petals spread in starlike (sometimes bell-
like) manner, and 8 stamens (4 of which may be
very small) close around the style. Leaves are
undivided, linear-cuneate; flowers are both
axillary and terminal. Flowers April to Nov.

Acacia celastrifolia
FAMILY Mimosaceae
A shrub 9 to 12 ft tall, with white (glaucous) stems. Phyllodes are 1 or 1½-in. long, broadly ovate with a sharp point arising from the rounded apex, and glaucous grey-green. The globular bright-yellow flower heads are borne on axillary and terminal panicles. Occurs on sandy soils in the Avon, Stirling and Eyre districts of south-western W.A. Flowering time is June to Dec.

Silky Kunzea   *Kunzea sericea*
FAMILY   Myrtaceae
One of two Western Australian *Kunzea* shrubs with large flowers that are borne on short bottle-brush-like spikes, this species has silky-surfaced, grey-green foliage and dwarfed, irregular habit of growth. It occurs on bare granite outcrops, growing from the rock crevices, southern interior to mid south-coastal W.A. (Avon, Eyre, Cool-gardie districts.) Flowering time is Oct. and Nov.

One-Sided Bottlebrush ▲
Calothamnus quadrifidus
FAMILY Myrtaceae
The genus *Calothamnus* (24 species) is not found outside WA. The flowers are arranged pre-dominantly along one side of the stem, and are more or less tubular, the stamens being united into flat bundles, which together form a tubular access to the nectar, and spread brushlike only at their outer end. This bushy shrub with long needle-like leaves occurs in many habitats throughout the southwest. Flowers July to Dec.

Rock-Loving Grevillea   ▶
Grevillea petrophiloi
FAMILY Proteaceae
Growing in Kalbarri National Park, this rounded shrub bears its many dusty-pink bottlebrush spikes on tall thin leafless flower stems. Leaves are much divided into long thin erect segments. Flowers, in dense racemes, are deep pink tipped with dark grey-green in the bud stage. Occurs central west-coastal, extendi inland (Irwin, Avon, Coolgardie districts). Flowering time is June to Sept.

Golden Feather-Flower *Verticordia chrysantha*
FAMILY Myrtaceae
The genus *Verticordia* is almost confined to
WA, where some 50 species occur. Many are
renowned for their springtime display. The
5 calyx lobes of each flower are fringed with
feather-like hairs or narrow lobes; petals also
are sometimes fringed, and filaments are united
into tube. Favours rocky hillsides. Widespread
through inland south-west WA. Flowering time
is Sept. to Nov.

Banksia ashbyi
FAMILY Proteaceae
A magnificent shrub or small tree 5 to 20 ft tall,
with spectacular deep-orange flower spikes up
to 12 in. long. Leaves are long (6 to 10 in.),
glabrous, flat, and deeply divided into numerous
triangular lobes. Flowers open out from base of
spike upwards; tips of long stiff styles do not
remain hooked on fully opened flowers. Grows
on central west-coastal WA. Flowering time is
May to Sept.

Petrophile divaricata
FAMILY Proteaceae
Flowers are clustered in terminal and axillary
heads; the style tip, which protrudes from each
opened perianth-tube, is covered in fine
reflexed hairs. Leaves are variable, much-
branched, with many wide-spreading pointed
segments (i.e. *divaricate*). Occurs near south
coast of WA (Stirling district). Flowers Sept. to
Nov.

Kalgan Boronia *Boronia heterophylla*
FAMILY Rutaceae
A compact shrub reaching 5 ft. Leaves are
usually 3-foliate on young plants, but lateral
pinnae are often dropped, the plants then
producing simple foliage. Young stems are
glabrous. Flowers are fragrant, and become pa
with age. Occurs in Kalgan and King River
districts on south coast near Albany. Flowering
time is Aug. to Nov.

Grevillea dielsiana
FAMILY Proteaceae
A rather prickly shrub with pendant racemes of
bright red flowers, which have very long
styles. Leaves are needle-like, dividing into
three spreading segments, each of which again
divides into three, terminating in sharp points.
The species occurs on west-coastal sand-heath
plains some 400 miles north of Perth. Flowering
time is July to Oct.

Red-Flowering Gum *Eucalyptus ficifolia*
FAMILY Myrtaceae
Probably the best known of all the Western
Australian flowering gums, this is a small,
densely foliaged tree to about 30 ft. high. The
bark is grey, rough. Leaves are usually large,
broadly lanceolate, dark glossy green above
Flower colour varies; deep crimson, pink, white.
Flowering is profuse, with many umbels (each
of 3 to 7 flowers) clustered together in large
terminal corymbs. It is native to a small area
on the south coast of WA, flowers Dec. to Feb.

Dryandra falcata ▶
FAMILY Proteaceae
Beneath the steep peaks of the Stirling Range
this dryandra, a low, densely foliaged prickly
shrub, comes into flower during October.
Leaves are longer than the flower head, cuneat
prickly-toothed at the ends; involucral bracts
are less than half as long as the flowers. Occur
south-coastal WA in rocky country.

Dryandra runcinata
FAMILY Proteaceae
A densely foliaged, compact low shrub, bearing flowers at, or within inches of the ground, where they are almost hidden. Leaves are long, thin, pinnatifid almost to the midrib. Flower heads 3 or 4 in. long, with many rows of bronzed involucral bracts; perianth limb (tip) hairy. Grows on rocky lateritic hilltips, forming dense, prickly low thickets, in south-west WA. Flowers Sept. to Nov.

Dryandra speciosa ▼
FAMILY Proteaceae
Grows as a dense shrub 3 to 15 ft tall, with flower-heads hanging downwards, half-hidden beneath the leafy apex of the supporting branchlet. A basal involucre of bracts is characteristic of the genus *Dryandra*.
This species grows on
sand heaths of inland south-west WA (Avon district). Flowers May to Sept.

Western Australian Christmas Tree ▶
Nuytsia floribunda
FAMILY Loranthaceae
The genus *Nuytsia* contains one species, confined to the south-west. It belongs to the mistletoe family, and retains to some degree the parasitic habit—its roots attach to those of other plants. Flowers, in large panicles, are tubular with 6 narrow perianth lobes and 6 stamens. The seed is winged, falls as soon as ripe, germinates easily; growth is slow and a host plant is needed. Flowering time is Nov. to Jan.

Spider Orchid   *Caladenia patersonii*
FAMILY   Orchidaceae
A slender terrestrial orchid 1 to 2 ft tall, flowers usually white with a few red-brown markings. Petals and sepals taper to long thin points. The labellum has 4 to 6 rows of calli. The Western Australian variety *longicaudata* has many exceptionally large flowers. Flowering time is Sept. to Oct.

Lemon Scent-Myrtle   *Darwinia citriodora* ▲
FAMILY   Myrtaceae
A tall shrub carrying small yet attractive flowers, enclosed within an involucre of 4 coloured bracts. There are 4 flowers to each head, and the reddish bracts are just long enough to conceal the flower petals but not the very long styles, which protrude well beyond the involucre. Occurs in granite country, south-western WA. Flowers July to Dec.

Golden Kangaroo-Paw   ▶
                          Anigosanthos pulcherrimu
FAMILY   Amaryllidaceae
This is one of WA's 9 kangaroo-paws. It is a perennial herbaceous plant 3 to 6 ft tall, with leaves densely felted, grey-green. The many golden-felted flowers are borne on a dichotomous branched pannicle. Each paw-like flower is a tubular perianth which splits open in a one-sided manner, revealing the 6 stamens and long style. They flower Dec. to Feb.

Protea-Like Dryandra   *Dryandra proteoides* ▼

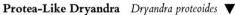

Many-Flowered Honeysuckle
Lambertia multiflora
FAMILY Proteaceae
A genus of 9 species, all confined to WA except for one in NSW. This small shrub occurs on stony ground, central west-coast and Darling Ranges of WA. Its involucres are terminal, 7-flowered clusters. Each flower is tubular, with the 4 perianth segments rolling back to leave the long style protruding. Leaves have a small sharp spiny tip. Flowering time is July to Sept.

Bronze Shell Orchid
Pterostylis scabra (syn. *P. constricta*)
FAMILY Orchidaceae
In this genus the middle sepal and two upper petals form a hood, or galea. The genus is notable for its sensitive hinged labellum, which springs against the galea to trap insects inside the hood (for pollination). This species is widely distributed through south-western WA. Flowering time is June to Aug.

Albany Bottlebrush *Callistemon speciosus*
FAMILY Myrtaceae
Deep red flower spikes 3 to 5 in. tall, long stiff lanceolate leaves, and strong rigid branches mak this a spectacular shrub. The flower's calyx is hirsute, leaves have noticeable lateral veins, differentiating it from *C. phoeniceus*, the only other south-western species. Occurs from the south coast northwards almost to Perth, in swampy places. Flowers Oct. to Mar.

Lechenaultia tubiflora
FAMILY Goodeniaceae
This leschenaultia forms a thick prostrate clum with short leafy stems bearing abundant red or creamy flowers. The almost total absence of wings to the corolla tube make this a distinctiv species, in appearance quite unlike most other leschenaultias. Occurs on white sand, mid west-coast, inland south-west. Flowering time is Sept. to Dec.

Verticordia etheliana
FAMILY Myrtaceae
Though many verticordias make spectacular displays en masse, others have fewer, larger flowers, which have great beauty in their intricate detail. The petals are finely fringed, calyx lobes are feathery, while around the central style is a radiating ring of stamens alternating with staminodes (sterile stamens). This slender 18 inch-tall shrub occurs on sand-heath plains of the mid west-coast of WA. Flowering time is Sept. to Nov.

A Pink Feather-Flower *Verticordia insignis*
FAMILY Myrtaceae
A small slender shrub 1 or 2 ft tall. Flowers are borne in wide corymbs. The 5 calyx lobes, finely divided and feather-like, spread wide beneath rounded, fringed petals; filaments are united into a short tube. The lanceolate leaves, in opposite pairs, are rather sparsely scattered. Occurs in stony areas throughout the south-west. Flowering time is Aug. to Oct.

Albany Pitcher Plant *Cephalotus follicularis*
FAMILY Cephalotaceae
These pitchers are modified leaves which, by means of slippery inner surfaces and incurved pallisade cause small insects to fall into a pool o liquid at the bottom. There they are 'digested' to provide additional plant nutrients. The family Cephalotaceae is endemic to WA; this sole species is confined to swampy localities along the south coast. Flowering time is Dec. to Feb. (The flowers, small and white, are not shown.)

Holly-leaved Banksia *Banksia ilicifolia*
FAMILY Proteaceae
Of the 50-odd banksia species the Holly-leaved
is unique. All have numerous small flowers
arranged around a central stem or axis to make
a dense cylindrical or globular head or spike—
except *Banksia ilicifolia*, which has flowers in a
head like that of a dryandra. Leaves are glossy
dark-green, toothed in holly-leaf fashion;
flowers are yellow, ageing to red. Occurs along
sandy coastal plains of the south-west. Flowering
time is Aug. to Oct.

White Plume Grevillea *Grevillea leucopteris*
FAMILY Proteaceae
A rounded, finely foliaged shrub to 15 ft tall,
with many large racemes of creamy-white,
strongly scented flowers held high on long bare
flower stems. Leaves are much-divided, with
narrow-linear segments. Each flower stem
branches to form a large terminal panicle of
many racemes, which in the bud stage are
covered in dusty-red bracts. Occurs on sand-
heath plains, mid west-coast (Irwin). Flowering
time is Sept. to Jan.

Yellow Everlasting *Helipterum stipitatum*
FAMILY Compositae
A small herbaceous plant growing to 18 in. tall.
Leaves hoary green-grey, mostly at base of
flower stem. Flower heads solitary, terminal,
about 1 to 1½ in. across. The flowers of the
composite head and the surrounding involucre
of bracts are rich yellow. Flowering time is
Aug. to Nov.

Melaleuca megacephala
FAMILY Myrtaceae
A large shrub, with tall, slender, upright, soft-
foliaged branches carrying large, globular,
terminal flower heads. Leaves are alternate,
obovate, up to 1 in. long, pubescent grey-green.
Individual flowers have their long staminal
bundles white or very pale yellow, tipped with
large orange-golden anthers. Occurs on sand
heath country, mid west-coastal WA.
Flowering time is Aug. to Oct.

COLLECTION AND PRESERVATION OF PLANT MATERIAL

There are several points to consider when collecting plant material for permanent retention in an herbarium collection. All naturalists waste a lot of time and have many disappointments until they learn a few simple techniques which help to bring some order into their activities. However, each person must use his own ingenuity to develop habits of work, and equipment which suit his personal requirements.

OBSERVATION

The first essential is to observe as closely as possible all features of the living plant in the field. The habitat or location, the size and form, and then details of leaves, stems, flowers and fruits. For observing smaller details a good hand lens, magnifying 8 or 10 times, is essential.

SELECTION OF MATERIAL

Many native plants are absolutely protected by law. All plants in national parks are protected. Collecting must be done carefully, with minimum damage to the plant. Although fragmentary pieces of a plant may sometimes be adequate for determination, such a fragment has no value in a permanent collection kept for comparative purposes. A good herbarium specimen should, in general, include as many parts of the parent plant as it is possible to collect at the one time. Therefore:

1. Collect the whole plant *if it is small*, pulling it up by the roots, except for orchids where the bulbs should be left to produce new flowers in future seasons, and for known rare or localised plants.

With larger plants such as shrubs and trees, and with those that spread over large areas by means of runners and rhizomes, it is impossible and unnecessary to collect the whole plant. In these cases:

2. Wherever possible select a portion of plant bearing *foliage, flowers, buds and fruits*. Although flowers and fruits are of prime importance, foliage is also necessary. Where foliage varies in size, shape or texture on the one plant this variation should be demonstrated by the materials selected.

Usually a specimen six inches to one foot in length is adequate, especially if it has flowers or buds. Fruits may be collected from older stems, or from the ground beneath the plant, and put in labelled envelopes. Fresh leafy specimens can be stored in plastic bags, secured by a rubber band. A slip of paper attached by sellotape, should show date and place of collection.

RECORDING

Unless you have a phenomenal memory, record all observations on the spot, at the time. Therefore, always carry a notebook, with a pencil *attached*.

1. Make brief notes on the *habit of the plant*, e.g. 'Tree 15 feet high, branches spreading, leaves drooping.'

2. Always record the *locality and date of collection, the collector's name* and the *situation* in which the plant was growing, e.g. 'In saturated mud at edge of swamp.' Some plants have definite habitat preferences.

FURTHER STUDY

A microscope is a great help for further study of plant structure. The botanical dissecting microscope is inexpensive and portable; it can easily be put in a pack or basket and taken out in the field if necessary. For higher magnification, say $\times 40$ or $\times 100$, a stereoscopic microscope is best. A basic unit costs about $50.00, and additional parts can be bought as finance permits. For indoor work at night a good microscope lamp is a great help.

IDENTIFICATION

For authoritative identification of plants, specimens may be sent to the Director, Royal Botanic Gardens and National Herbarium in New South Wales and Victoria; the State Herbarium in Queensland, South Australia and Western Australia; the Department of Botany at the University of Tasmania; the Northern Territory Administration Botanist, Darwin.

PRESERVATION OF MATERIAL

Specimens can be preserved without much trouble by pressing between layers of dry newspaper. To prepare a plant, place between sheets of newspaper and apply an even, medium pressure. Excessive pressure will burst and squash soft parts, while inadequate pressure allows material to wilt, wrinkle and curl within the papers.

Before applying pressure smooth out the plant parts on the sheet of paper in order to display them to the best advantage. If specimens are too bulky, trim off any excessive foliage, or hard thorny branches, from the back and front of the specimen so that it will be as flat as possible. Delicate parts of a specimen can be well displayed if foam plastic is placed over them while drying.

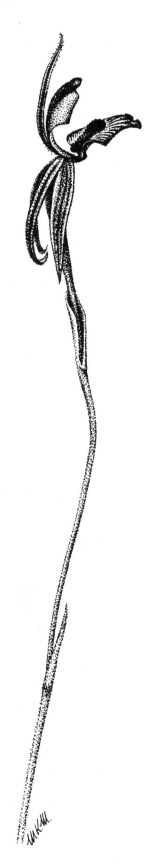

Zebra Orchid *Caladenia cairnsiana*
FAMILY Orchidaceae
Colour: dark stripes on very pale labellum, petals, sepals. Occurrence: southern WA.
Flowering: Aug. to Oct.

PROTECTED PLANTS

Most States have Wildflower Protection Acts aimed at safeguarding certain plants, the beauty and rarity of which expose them to vandalism, while Forestry Departments and National Park committees usually prohibit the removal of all wildflowers from their reserves.

Isotoma *Isotoma hypocrateriformis*
FAMILY Lobeliaceae
Colour: variable, deep mauve, pink, or white.
Occurrence: sandy or gravelly soils, south-west of WA. Flowering: Nov. to Dec.

VICTORIA

List of Wildflowers or Native Plants Protected under the *Wild Flowers and Native Plants Protection Act* 1958.

BOTANICAL NAME	VERNACULAR NAME
Acacia	Wattles—all species except *Acacia armata*
Aciphylla glacialis	Snow Aciphyll
Alyxia buxifolia	Sea Box
Banksia	Banksia—all species
Boronia	Boronias—all species
Bossiaea walkeri	Cactus Pea
Brunonia australis	Blue Pincushion
Calectasia cyanea	Blue Tinsel-Lily
Calostemma purpureum	Garland Lily
Calytrix	Fringe-myrtles—all species
Celmisia	Silver Daisies—all species
Cheiranthera linearis	Finger flower
Correa	Correas or Native Fuchsias—all species
Crinum flaccidum	Darling or Murray Lily
Epacris impressa	Common Heath—the State floral emblem
Eremophila	Emu-bushes—all species
Eriostemon	Wax-flowers—all species
Gaultheria appressa	Waxberry
Gompholobium	Wedge-peas—all species
Grevillea	Grevilleas—all species
Hardenbergia violacea	False Sarsaparilla or Purple Coral-pea
Helichrysum acuminatum	Orange Everlasting
Helichrysum bracteatum	Golden Everlasting
Howittia trilocularis	Blue Howittia
Lhotzkya alpestris	Snow Myrtle
Livistona australis	Cabbage Fan-palm
Micromyrtus ciliatus	Fringed Heath-myrtle
Melaleuca squamea	Mealy Honey-myrtle
Melaleuca wilsonii	Violet Honey-myrtle
Olearia frostii	Bogong Daisy-bush
Orchidaceae	Orchids—all species
Oxalis lactea	White Wood-sorrel
Prostanthera	Mint-bushes—all species
Pteridophyta	Clubmosses, ferns and fern allies—all species *except bracken*
Stylidium graminifolium	Trigger-plant
Telopea oreades	Gippsland Waratah
Thryptomene	Heath-myrtles or Thryptomenes—all species
Thysanotus tuberosus	Fringe-lily
Wittsteinia vacciniacea	Baw Baw Berry

Red Beaks *Lyperanthus nigricans*
FAMILY Orchidaceae
Colour: white or orange-pink extensively streaked with dark crimson and brown.
Occurrence: on heaths of all states except Qld.
Flowering: blooms most prolifically after fire, Sept. to Oct.

TASMANIA

Under provisions of the *Scenery Preservation Act* all flora in those areas proclaimed as national parks, scenic reserves, etc., is protected regardless of species.

SOUTH AUSTRALIA

Flora is protected under the *Native Plants Protection Act* 1939. No plant, shrub or tree indigenous to South Australia may be gathered, plucked, cut, pulled up, destroyed, removed or injured during the proclaimed protected period on any crown lands, land reserved for a public purpose, any street or road, any forest reserve (except under licence or other authority), or any private land unless permission from owner or lessee is first obtained. The selling of wildflowers or protected native plants is forbidden. The minister may issue licences authorizing the picking of wildflowers for scientific or other purposes.

WESTERN AUSTRALIA

In WA, rather than a list of protected flowers, *all* wildflowers of certain areas are protected. *All* wildflowers and native plants in those parts of Western Australia described hereunder are protected under the *Native Flora Protection Act*.

(a) All crown lands, state forests, lands reserved for a public purpose under the provisions of the Land Act and every road within the South-West and Eucla Divisions of the State, and
(b) outside the South-West and Eucla Divisions of the State, the lands reserved for the protection of indigenous flora or fauna.
(The South-West and Eucla Divisions of WA are marked on maps pages 120-1.)

NORTHERN TERRITORY

All flora is protected on national parks, flora and fauna reserves, and other areas under control of the Northern Territory Reserves Board. The wildlife sanctuaries and large Aboriginal reserves also provide effective flora preservation as entry to these areas is restricted. By far the greatest part of the Northern Territory is used for grazing of livestock, using the native flora, which through most of the centre has deteriorated under the combined effects of drought and over-grazing. In this respect conservation of the native flora is vital to the entire arid and semi-arid zone (the greater part of this continent) because there is every indication that under mismanagement by the pastoral industry vast areas could deteriorate until the trend becomes irreversible and dustbowl conditions prevail.

SPECIFIED AREAS

The legislation provides for the declaration of certain plants in specified districts as protected native plants. There are lists of protected plants for Bishop Island in Moreton Bay, and Friday Island in Torres Strait.

NEW SOUTH WALES

Under the provisions of the *Wild Flowers and Native Plants Protection Act*, 1927–1967, the following were declared protected for the period 1st July 1968 to 30th June 1970.

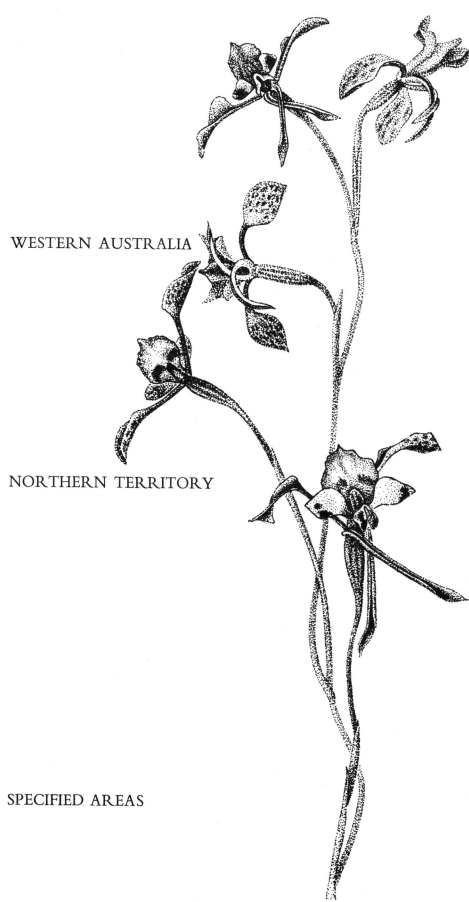

Tiger Orchid *Diuris sulphurea*
FAMILY Orchidaceae
Colour: yellow with several brown spots and markings on the labellum. Occurrence: south-eastern Aust.

NEW SOUTH WALES
(Continued)

SEED PLANTS	
BOTANICAL NAME	VERNACULAR NAME
Actinotus helianthi	Flannel Flower
Archontophoenix cunninghamiana	Bangalow Palm
Blandfordia— all indigenous speci s	Christmas Bells
Boronia— all indigenous species	Boronia
Bulbophyllum— all indigenous species	Orchid
Calanthe triplicata	Orchid
Callistemon acuminatus	Tapering-leaved Bottlebrush
Callistemon citrinus	Red Bottlebrush
Callistemon linearifolius	Narrow-leaved Bottlebrush
Callistemon rigidus	Stiff-leaved Bottlebrush
Casuarina cunninghamiana	River Oak
Caustis— all indigenous species	Curley Sedge
Ceratopetalum gummiferum	Christmas Bush
Clianthus formosus	Sturt's Desert Pea
Crowea— all indigenous species	Crowea
Cymbidium— all indigenous species	Orchid
Dendrobium— all indigenous species	Orchid
Dipodium— all indigenous species	Orchid
Doryanthes— all indigenous species	Giant Lily
Eriostemon— all indigenous species	Wax Plant
Galeola— all indigenous species	Orchid
Geodorum pictum	Orchid
Grevillea aspleniifolia	Fern-leaved Grevillea
Grevillea caleyi	Caley's Grevillea
Grevillea longifolia	Fern-leaved Grevillea
Liparis— all indigenous species	Orchid
Livistona australis	Cabbage Tree Palm
Lomatia silaifolia	Crinkle Bush
Microstrobos fitzgeraldii	
Oberonia— all indigenous species	Orchid
Papillilabium beckleri	Orchid
Parasarcochilus— all indigenous species	
Peristeranthus hillii	Orchid
Persoonia pinifolia	Pine-leaved Geebung
Phaius tankervilliae	Orchid
Phreatia— all indigenous species	Orchid
Plectorrhiza— all indigenous species	Orchid
Rhinerrhiza divitiflora	Orchid
Sarcochilus— all indigenous species	Orchid
Schistotylus purpuratus	Orchid
Sprengelia incarnata	Sprengelia
Taeniophyllum— all indigenous species	Orchid
Telopea— all indigenous species	Waratah
Xylomelum— all indigenous species	Woody Pear

FERNS AND FERN ALLIES	
BOTANICAL NAME	VERNACULAR NAME
Adiantum— all indigenous species	Maiden Hair Fern
Asplenium nidus	Bird's Nest Fern
Asplenium falcatum	
Cyathea— all indigenous species	Tree Fern
Davillia pyxidata	Hare's Foot Fern
Dicksonia— all indigenous species	Tree Fern
Lycopodium deuterodensum	Mountain Moss
Platycerium— all indigenous species	Elk Horn and Stag Horn
Tmesipteris— all indigenous species	
Todea barbara	Tree Fern

In addition, all flora is protected in national parks, state parks and similarly reserved public lands.

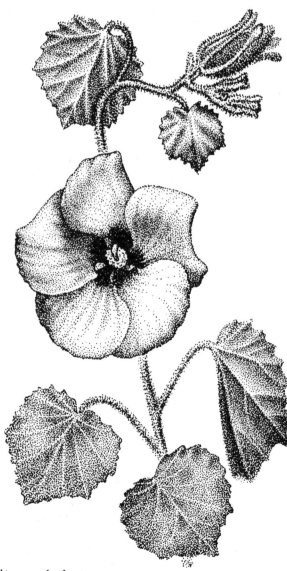

Hibiscus panduriformis
FAMILY Malvaceae
Colour: deep rich yellow with dark red centre.
Occurrence: Kimberleys of WA.
Flowering: Aug. to Sept.

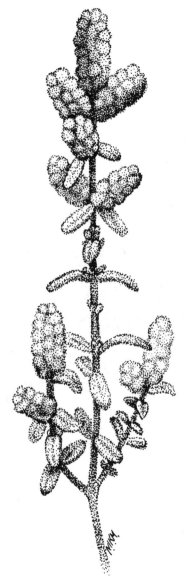

Lamb's Tails *Lachynostachys brevispicata*
FAMILY Verbenaceae
Colour: spikes white, woolly, with small lilac flowers embedded. Occurrence: on red sand, interior of WA to NT.
Flowering: July to Oct.

The plants listed may not be picked on any Crown land, State Forest, public park, road or land dedicated or reserved for public purpose. With regard to private land, protected native plants may only be collected with the owner's or lessee's permission.

FERNS

BOTANICAL NAME	VERNACULAR NAME
Adiantum aethiopicum	Common Maidenhair Fern
Adiantum formosum	Scrub Maidenhair Fern
Adiantum hispidulum	Five-fingered Maidenhair Fern
Adiantum lunulatum	Kidney Maidenhair Fern
Alsophila australis	Tree Fern
Alsophila baileyana	Wig Tree Fern
Alsophila excelsa	Tall Tree Fern
Alsophila leichhardtiana	Prickly Tree Fern
Alsophila robertsoniana	Robertson's Tree Fern
Alsophila rebeccae	Broad-leaved Tree Fern
Asplenium laserpitiifolium	Johnston R. Maidenhair Fern
Asplenium nidus	Bird's Nest Fern
Asplenium simplicifrons	Narrow-leaved Bird's Nest Fern
Davallia pyxidata	Hare's Foot Fern
Dicksonia antarctica	Mountain Tree Fern
Dicksonia youngiae	Young's Tree Fern
Lygodium spp.	Climbing Maidenhair Ferns—all species
Ophioglossum pendulum	Ribbon Fern
Platycerium grande	Staghorn Fern
Platycerium alcicorne (P. bifurcatum)	Elkhorn Fern
Pteris spp.—all species	
Vittaria elongata	Bootlace Fern

PALMS

Archontophoenix alexandre (A. alexandrae)	Northern Piccabean
Archontophoenix cunninghamii	Southern Piccabean
Bacularia monostachya (Linospadix monostachyus)	Walking-stick Palm
Drymophloeus normanbyi (Normanbya normanbyi)	Black Palm
Licuala muelleri (L. ramsayi)	Fan Palm
Livistona australis	Cabbage Tree Palm

ORCHIDS

Calanthe veratrifolia	Scrub Lily
Cymbidium albuciflorum	Long-leaved Arrowroot Orchid
Cymbidium canaliculatum	Arrowroot Orchid
Cymbidium sparkesii	Black Orchid
Cymbidium suave	Slender Arrowroot Orchid
Dendrobium aemulum	Box-tree Orchid
Dendrobium beckleri	Small Pencil Orchid
Dendrobium bigibbum	Cooktown Orchid
Dendrobium canaliculatum	Tree Tree Orchid
Dendrobium delicatum	
Dendrobium fusiforme	
Dendrobium gracilicaule	Slender Orchid
Dendrobium johannis	Golden Orchid
Dendrobium kingianum	

Dendrobium linguiforme	Tongue Orchid
Dendrobium phalaenopsis (D. bigibbum var. phalaenopsis)	Large Purple Orchid
Dendrobium smilliae	Bottle Brush Orchid
Dendrobium speciosum	King Orchid or Rock Lily
Dendrobium superbiens	Torres Strait Orchid
Dendrobium teretifolium	Pencil Orchid
Dendrobium tetragonum	Spider Orchid
Dendrobium toftii	
Dendrobium undulatum	Curly Orchid
Eria fitzalannii	
Oberonia spp.	Soldier's Crest Orchid—all species
Phaius bernaysii (P. australis var. bernaysii)	Yellow Phaius
Phaius grandifolius (P. tankervilliae)	Common Phaius
Phalaenopsis amabilis	
Phalaenopsis rosenstromii (P. amabilis var. rosenstromii)	
Pholidota imbricata	Banana Orchid
Sarcochilus fitzgeraldii	
Sarcochilus hartmanii	

MISCELLANEOUS PLANTS

Blandfordia spp.	Christmas Bells—all species
Boronia spp.	Boronia
Cordyline terminalis (Cordyline spp.)	Palm Lily
Dischidia nummularia	Button Orchid
Eurycles amboinensis	Cairns Lily or Cardwell Lily
Helichrysum	Everlastings
Helipterum	Everlastings
Hoya australis	Hoya or Wax Flower
Lycopodium phlegmaria	Tassel Fern
Lycopodium spp.	All Lycopods and Tassel Ferns
Myrmecodia antoinii	Ant Orchid
Rhododendron lochae	
Selaginella spp.—all species	
Sowerbaea juncea	Vanilla Lily

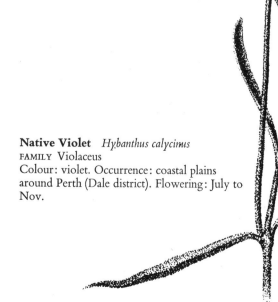

Native Violet *Hybanthus calycinus*
FAMILY Violaceus
Colour: violet. Occurrence: coastal plains around Perth (Dale district). Flowering: July to Nov.

CULTIVATION OF WILDFLOWERS

In recent years the cultivation of Australian plants has attracted great interest, and many gardens now have at least a few of Australia's own shrubs or small ornamental trees, while others contain exclusively native plants.

An Australian wildflower garden may be established on a completely bare, cleared block of land, though it is an advantage beginning if possible by retaining natural vegetation of trees, undergrowth, on the site; the bush garden may be planned around any attractive natural features such as rock outcrops or a creek. The layout is usually 'informal' with trees and shrubs in irregular, natural-looking clumps, smaller ground-cover plants beneath, the ground scattered with leaves, gravel, sometimes sawdust to retain moisture, keep roots cool, minimize weeds and provide humus. Paths and artificial structures are usually kept inconspicuous.

When choosing native plants it is wise to select those which come from an environment not too dissimilar to that of the planned garden, though many of our natives will grow in a wide variety of soils and climates. It is worth considering the origin of each species. A wildflower from the Western Australian sandplains may not be a success if planted on heavy, often-waterlogged clay, in a more humid environment. Nor can rainforest species, whose leaves need a sheltered, humid atmosphere, be expected to flourish in the dry-heat climate that is usual in much of South Australia, Western Australia and the inland.

Many of the spectacular Western Australian wildflowers are native to well-drained sand-

Running Postman *Kennedia prostrata*
FAMILY Papilionaceae
Colour: scarlet with yellow centre.
Occurrence: temperate regions of all states.
Flowering: Sept. to Nov.

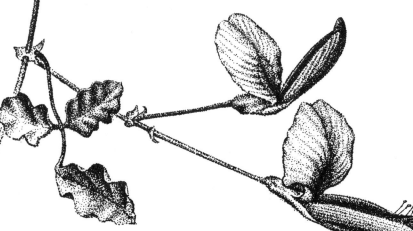

plain areas with an average annual rainfall of 20 inches down to 10 inches. Their success when planted on rich soils in coastal regions of heavier rainfall varies greatly, the small ornamental eucalypts being perhaps easier than the sandplain banksias; this calls for an experimental approach at times.

Poor drainage in heavy soils often causes failures. By installing deep drains (rubble-stone or agricultural pipes) to lower the water table, or by building up some garden beds, it is usually possible to grow quite a wide variety of native plants.

In an established native garden watering is often completely unnecessary except for new plantings, or for the smaller species through long dry periods. New plants should be given a long soaking at infrequent intervals—a hose left trickling all day or over-night, once a week, later once a fortnight, so that the roots will penetrate very deeply to follow the disappearing water. (Frequent brief waterings keep roots near the surface, making even a large shrub incapable of withstanding a dry period without water being given.) After the first year or two watering will be unnecessary, except for humid-environment plants being grown in dry conditions.

Many species, particularly grevilleas, banksias and eucalypts produce copious quantities of nectar, as they depend wholly or in part upon birds for the transfer of pollen. The native garden is, therefore, likely to attract many nectar-eating birds, as well as insectivorous species that hunt on foliage and flowers. While some minor insect damage is usually experienced when plants are small this seems to become negligible as shrubs and trees mature and birds become resident, or frequent visitors—which they will not if poison sprays and dusts are continuously applied.

Many nurseries stock a range of native plants, particularly the small ornamental eucalypts and bottlebrushes, while a considerable number in all states now concentrate exclusively upon Australian plants and ornamental trees suitable for small gardens. It is possible also to collect seed and cultivate it. Some may be grown from cuttings, while others may be transplanted when very small. But plants should not be taken from our diminishing bushland unless it is known that destruction for 'development' is inevitable, when transplanting becomes a valuable way of saving some that otherwise would be destroyed.

For anyone planning a native garden, or a wildflower section within their garden, the journal *Australian Plants*, published by the Society for Growing Australian Plants, 250 Picnic Point Road, Picnic Point, NSW, will give much useful information, together with lists of native plant nurseries in all states.

NATIONAL PARKS AND WILDFLOWER RESERVES

Although the law in most states forbids the picking of all or certain wildflowers on crown land, roadsides and various other places, far greater damage is being caused by complete destruction of the natural environment in clearing, burning, mining and similar 'developmental' activities. Compared with the millions of acres that every year are totally and permanently denuded of all native vegetation the picking of wildflowers (except on a large scale for commercial sales) is insignificant. Only in national parks and similar reserves is there a chance that these wildflowers will always be a feature of the Australian environment. The list of parks with a rich or interesting flora which is included within each section is condensed from Michael Morcombe's *Australia's National Parks* (Melbourne, Lansdowne, 1969) where there appears much more information, road access maps and some 120 colour plates of this continent's parks and nature reserves.

THE NORTH
W.A., N.T., QLD.

THE NORTH-EAST
QLD., N.S.W.

THE CENTRE
W.A., N.T.. S.A., N.S.W., QLD., VIC.

THE SOUTH-WEST
W.A.

THE EAST
N.S.W., A.C.T., QLD.

THE SOUTH
S.A., VIC., N.S.W., TAS.

The sections of this book are based upon natural vegetation regions. These in turn are influenced by amount and season of rainfall, soils, and isolation by desert or sea.

There is of course considerable overlap between the section regions. Some plant species have a distribution extending far beyond the boundaries of the section for which they are shown, while others are confined to very small areas, sometimes even to a single mountain peak.

THE NORTH-EAST includes the rain-forests, which extend into north-eastern New South Wales, overlapping by many hundreds of miles the east-coastal section. The latter includes the wildflower-rich Queensland 'granite belt', and the Noosa–Cooloola coastal plains, so that within this large geographical overlap each section covers its own distinctive vegetation regions.

The arid central (Eremaean) region is so extensive that many of the species shown in THE CENTRE occur in dry parts of all mainland states.

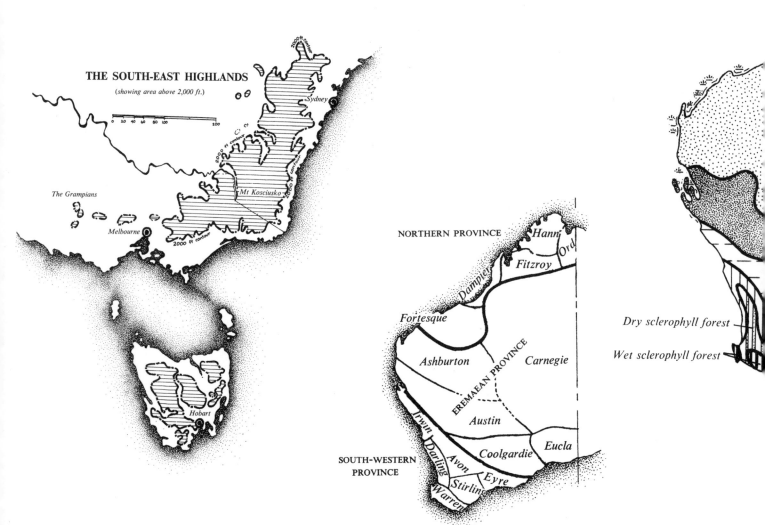

THE SOUTH-EAST HIGHLANDS
(showing area above 2,000 ft.)

The Grampians

Melbourne

Sydney

Mt Kosciusko

Hobart

NORTHERN PROVINCE

Hann
Ord
Fitzroy
Dampier
Fortesque
Ashburton
Carnegie
EREMAEAN PROVINCE
Austin
Coolgardie
Eucla
Irwin
Darling
Avon
Eyre
Stirling
Warren

SOUTH-WESTERN PROVINCE

Dry sclerophyll forest
Wet sclerophyll forest

WESTERN AUSTRALIA
Botanic Provinces and Districts

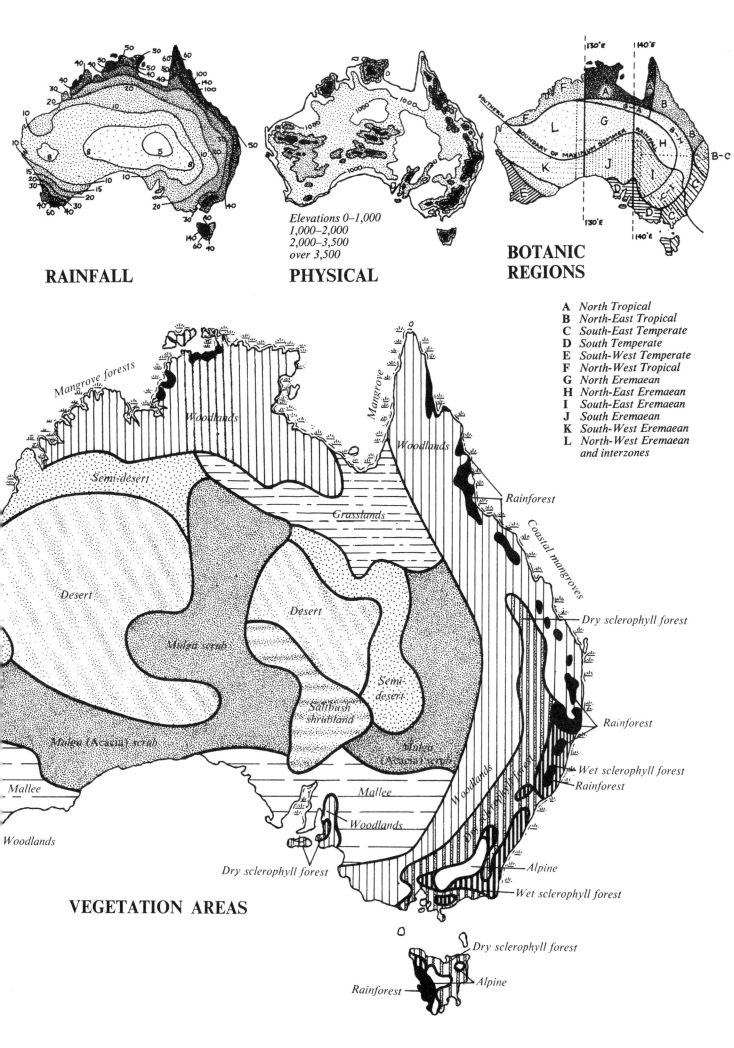

RAINFALL

Elevations 0–1,000
1,000–2,000
2,000–3,500
over 3,500

PHYSICAL

BOTANIC REGIONS

A North Tropical
B North-East Tropical
C South-East Temperate
D South Temperate
E South-West Temperate
F North-West Tropical
G North Eremaean
H North-East Eremaean
I South-East Eremaean
J South Eremaean
K South-West Eremaean
L North-West Eremaean
   and interzones

Mangrove forests

Woodlands

Semi-desert

Grasslands

Mangrove

Woodlands

Rainforest

Coastal mangroves

Desert

Desert

Dry sclerophyll forest

Mulga scrub

Semi-desert

Rainforest

Saltbush shrubland

Mulga (Acacia) scrub

Mulga (Acacia) scrub

Wet sclerophyll forest

Rainforest

Mallee

Mallee

Woodlands

Woodlands

Woodlands

Alpine

Dry sclerophyll forest

Wet sclerophyll forest

VEGETATION AREAS

Dry sclerophyll forest

Alpine

Rainforest

GLOSSARY

ACUMINATE, tapering to a slender point (leaf).

ALTERNATE, as of leaves inserted at different heights along stems, or of stamens present between petals.

ANTHER, that part of a stamen which contains the pollen.

ARTICULATE, jointed.

AWN, a fine, bristle-like appendage.

AXIL, the point or angle between a branch and leaf.

AXILLARY, a flower or inflorescence arising from an axil.

BEAK, prominent prolongation of a fruit.

BERRY, a succulent indehiscent fruit with seeds immersed in pulp.

BIENNIAL, a plant that requires two years to complete its life cycle from seed germination to seed production, flowering and death.

BIFID, dividing into two for about half its length.

BIPINNATE, twice pinnate (see pinnate).

BISEXUAL, with both male (stamens) and female (pistil) organs in the same flower.

BRACT, a modified leaf that encloses or embraces in its axil a flower or inflorescence.

CALLI, glandular hairs (as on labellum of many orchids).

CALYX, the outer whorl of a flower, consisting of free or united sepals.

CAMPANULATE, bell-shaped.

CAPSULE, a dry fruit of two or more united carpels that open when ripe to liberate the seeds.

CILIATE, fringed with hairs or 'cilia'.

CLAVATE, club-shaped.

COLUMN, the stamens and style when combined in a solid body as in orchids and triggerplants.

CORDATE, heart-shaped, with a notch towards the stem (leaf).

COMPOUND LEAF, a leaf of two or more leaflets.

COROLLA, the inner whorl of a flower consisting of free or united petals.

CORYMB, a raceme in which the flower stalks branch at different levels but the flowers rise to approximately the same level as in a flat head.

COTYLEDON, a seed leaf, present in the embryo plant, that serves as a food reservoir.

CRENATE, margin cut into blunt or rounded teeth.

CUNEATE, wedge-shaped, with narrow end to stem (leaves or petals).

DECIDUOUS, falling off in a certain season.

DEFLEXED, bent downwards.

DEHISCENT, opening when ripe (applied to fruits).

DENTATE, finely toothed.

DICHOTOMOUS, divided into two branches, and again into two, and so on.

DISC-FLORET, flowers (usually tubular) in the centre of the composite flowers of some of the family Compositae.

ELLIPTICAL, oblong with regular rounded ends.

EMARGINATE, notched at the end.

ENDEMIC, peculiar to the region, state or continent and not native elsewhere.

ENTIRE, margins (of leaves, petals) without indentations, lobes, teeth.

EPICALYX, a calyx-like structure outside but close to the true calyx.

EPIPHYTE, a plant growing attached or lodged (but not parasitic) on another plant or object.

ERECT, standing vertically above ground.

FALCATE, curved like the blade of a scythe.

FILAMENT, threadlike stalk of a stamen, at the tip of which is the pollen-bearing anther.

FLORET, a small flower, part of a composite head.

FOLIOLATE, bearing leaflets.

FOLLICLE, a dry one-celled fruit consisting of a single carpel that splits and opens along one edge.

FRUIT, seed-bearing part of plant, developing from ovary.

GALEA, a petal shaped like a helmet.

GENUS, a group of species that resemble each other.

GLABROUS, having a shining surface without hairs.

GLAND, a wart-like prominence or appendage usually secreting a fluid.

GLAUCOUS, of an ash-grey, whitish or bluish tint, whitish powdery substance or 'bloom' which rubs off.

GLUTINOUS, sticky.

GYMNOSPERMS, plants whose seed vessels are not contained in a seed vessel or ovary, the pines and cycads.

GYNOECIUM, all the carpels of one flower.

HABITAT, the environment of a living plant, its natural home.

HASTATE, shaped like an arrow head.

HEAD, an inflorescence of sessile flowers, crowded together in a compact cluster and usually surrounded by an involucre (Compositae family).

HEATH, an open area, mostly flat, whose plant community consists chiefly of small shrubs with very small leaves.

HERB, a plant that does not develop a woody stem.

HERBACEOUS, a green, more or less soft type of plant.

HERMAPHRODITE, bearing both male and female reproductive organs.

HIRSUTE, covered with hairs, usually long, rather stiff.

HOARY, densely covered with almost microscopic hairs, giving a white or greyish appearance.

HYBRID, the progeny of two plants of different species.

IMBRICATE, with the edges overlapping.

INDUMENTUM, hairy with rather heavy covering.

INFLORESCENCE, the general grouping of flowers on a stem, the 'cluster'.

INVOLUCRE, a whorl of bracts surrounding the head of a flower, and rising from its base.

INVOLUTE, rolled inwards from both sides (usually a leaf).

KEEL, applied to the two front united petals of the 'pea' flowers.

KINO, gum exuded from bark of trees.

LABELLUM, the lip or lowest front-placed petal of an orchid.

LANCEOLATE, shaped like a spear head.

LIGULE, the one-sided, strap-shaped limb of the corolla, as in the corolla of ray florets of the Compositae family.

LINEAR, long and narrow with edges parallel (leaf).

LOBE, the projection between divisions of a leaf, petal or sepal.

LOCULUS, compartment within an ovary.

MALLEE, eucalypt with bulbous rootstock from which many stems arise.

MUCRONATE, with a sharp spiny tip.

NODE, part of stem from which leaves and other stems grow.

OBLANCEOLATE, inversely lanceolate, narrow end towards stem.

OBLONG, sides nearly parallel except at ends (leaf).

OBOVATE, inversely ovate, narrow end toward stem.

OPERCULUM, a cap or lid (as in Eucalyptus buds).

OVATE, roughly egg-shaped, broader end towards stem.

PALMATE, palm-shaped, like the fingers of a hand.

PANICLE, a much-branched inflorescence, each branch having several flowers.

PAPILIONACEOUS, applied to a form of flower found in most leguminous plants, having an irregular corolla consisting of a large upper petal, two lateral petals and two narrow lower petals between these (a butterfly likeness).

PAPPUS, ring of fine hairs crowning fruit of compositae.

PARASITIC, a plant which grows upon another, obtaining its nourishment from it, e.g. Mistletoe, Nuytsia.

PEDUNCLE, the stalk of an inflorescence, or of an individual flower when only one flower is present.

PERENNIAL, a plant that lives for a number of years.

PERIANTH, a single term for calyx and corolla, particularly applied to flowers where the two whorls appear as one.

PERSISTENT, applies to parts of the flower that remain after flowering

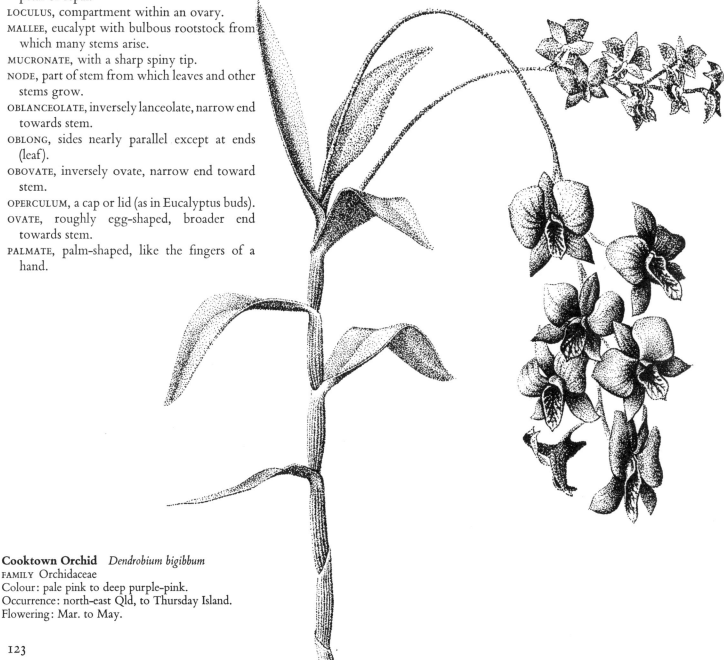

Cooktown Orchid   *Dendrobium bigibbum*
FAMILY Orchidaceae
Colour: pale pink to deep purple-pink.
Occurrence: north-east Qld, to Thursday Island.
Flowering: Mar. to May.

PETAL, one of the parts of the corolla, generally coloured.

PETALOID, resembling a petal.

PETIOLE, leaf stalk.

PETIOLATE, applied to leaves which have a petiole.

PHYLLODE, a leaf-like petiole which does not give rise to a leaf blade, a modification which occurs often in acacias.

PINNATE, a compound leaf having the leaflets arranged in a feather-like manner, arranged each side of a common leaf stalk (rachis).

PISTIL, otherwise known as the gynoecium, consisting of a stigma, style and ovary.

PITCHER, a tubular or cup-shaped vessel, the terminal portion of a leaf blade; may contain a digestive fluid.

POLLINIUM, (plural POLLINA) a mass of cohering pollen grains.

PROCUMBENT, trailing along the ground but not necessarily prostrate or rooting along stems.

PROSTRATE, fairly closely pressed to the ground, trailing.

PSEUDOBULB, the swollen bulbous-like stem of many epiphytic orchids.

PUBESCENT, covered with short, soft downy hairs.

PUNGENT, ending in a stiff, sharp point or tip.

RACEME, an inflorescence of stalked flowers arranged along an unbranched stem, the main axis of which continues to grow.

RAINFOREST, a dense forest dominated by soft-leaved trees with lianas and woody epiphytes.

RAY, all the ligulate flowers in the capitulum of a compositae (ray florets).

RECEPTACLE, the end of the flower stalk bearing the reproductive structures.

REVOLUTE, rolled backwards.

RHIZOME, underground stem.

ROSTRATE, beaked.

SAGITTATE, shaped like an arrow head.

SCABROUS, rough to the touch, usually due to short stiff hairs.

SCALE, a rudimentary leaf; a thin membranous expansion.

SCLEROPHYLLOUS, hard or leathery; leaves usually with thick cuticles and sunken stomata.

SCURFY, covered with minute loose scales.

SERRATE, toothed like a saw, with the teeth pointing forward.

SESSILE, without a stalk, applied to flowers and leaves which arise from the stem.

SHEATH, tubular structure, often at base of leaf.

SHRUB, a woody perennial that usually has several stems arising at, or near the ground, giving the plant a bushy appearance.

SIMPLE, undivided.

SINUATE, having a wavy outline.

SINUS, the recess between two lobes of a leaf (or organ).

SPATHULATE, spoon-shaped (leaf); broadest at the outer end, narrowing towards the stem end.

SPIKE, an arrangement of sessile flowers along an undivided stem.

STAMEN, the male organ of seed-forming plants, consisting of the pollen-bearing anther supported by the filament.

STIGMA, the part of the pistil that receives the pollen.

STANDARD, the broad upright petal of a papilionaceous flower.

STIPE, small stalk.

STYLE, the stalk joining the stigma to the ovary of the pistil.

SUCCULENT, juicy.

TERETE, cylindrical and slightly tapering (refers to leaves).

TERMINAL, borne at the end of a stem or branch.

TOMENTOSE (TOMENTUM), densely covered with short soft matted hairs.

TRIFOLIATE, having three leaves.

TRUNCATE, as if cut off sharply, squarely and abruptly.

TWINER, a plant which climbs by means of the stem, which twists around an adjoining object.

UMBEL, an arrangement of flowers in which a number of flower stalks arise from the same point.

VALVATE (of petals in bud), with the edges touching but not overlapping.

VALVE, one of the pieces formed by the vertical splitting of capsular fruits to allow the seed to escape.

VARIETY (VAR.), a sub-division of a species.

VENATION, the way in which the veins of leaves are arranged.

VILLOUS, covered with long, soft hairs.

VISCID, sticky.

WHORL, an arrangement of organs (flowers, leaves, stems) arising from the same node in a circle around an axis.

WING, any kind of flat membranous expansion; also, each of the two lateral petals of papilionaceous flowers.

XEROPHYTE, a drought-resistant plant.

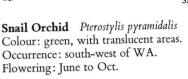

Snail Orchid *Pterostylis pyramidalis*
Colour: green, with translucent areas.
Occurrence: south-west of WA.
Flowering: June to Oct.

BIBLIOGRAPHY

Anderson, R. H., *The Trees of New South Wales*. Sydney, Govt. Printer, 1956.
Australian Plants quarterly journal published by Society for Growing Australian Plants, 860 Henry Lawson Drive, Picnic Point, NSW 2213.

Beadle, N. C. W., Evans, O. D., Carolin, R. O., *Handbook of the Vascular Plants of the Sydney District and Blue Mountains*. Armidale, University of New England, 1962.
Beard, J. S., *Descriptive Catalogue of West Australian Plants*. Sydney, Society for Growing Australian Plants, and Perth, Kings Park Board.
Black, J. M., *Flora of South Australia*. Adelaide, South Australian Govt. Printer, 2nd ed, 1957.
Blackall, W. E., *A Key to the Wildflowers of Western Australia*. Perth, University of Western Australia Press.
Blackall, W. E., Grieve, B. J., *How to Know Western Australian Wildflowers*. Parts 1 to 3. Perth, University of Western Australia Press, 1965.
Blakely, W. F., *A Key to the Eucalypts*. Canberra, Forestry & Timber Bureau, 1955.
Blombery, A. M., *A Guide to Native Australian Plants*. Sydney, Angus & Robertson, 1967.
Burbidge, N. T., *The Wattles of the Australian Capital Territory*. Canberra, Verity Hewitt, 1961.
Burbidge, N. T., *Dictionary of Australian Plant Genera*. Sydney, Angus & Robertson.

Child, John, *Australian Alpine Life*. Melbourne, Periwinkle Books, 1969.
Child, John, *Wildflowers of the Sydney Region*. Melbourne, Periwinkle Books, 1969.
Cochrane, G. R., Fuhrer, B. A., Rotherham, E. R., Willis, J. H., *Flowers and Plants of Victoria*. Sydney, A. H. & A. W. Reed, 1968.
Conservation Committee, Royal Society of Western Australia, *Nature Reserves & National Parks in Western Australia*. Perth, National Parks Board of Western Australia.
Costermans, L. F., *Trees of Victoria*. Melbourne, L. F. Costermans, 1966.
Curtis, Winifred M., *The Student's Flora of Tasmania* Parts 1, 2 and 3. Hobart, Govt. Printer, 1956–1967.

Davey, Keith, *Australian Desert Life*. Melbourne, Periwinkle Books, 1969.
Dockrill, A. W., *Australian Indigenous Orchids*, Vol. 1, 1969.

Erickson, R., *Orchids of the West*. 2nd ed, Perth, Paterson Brokensha, 1968.
Erickson, R., *Triggerplants*. Perth, Paterson Brokensha, 1958.
Erickson, R., *Plants of Prey*. Osborne Park (W.A.), Lamb Publications, 1968.
Ewart, Alfred J., *Flora of Victoria*. Melbourne, Victorian Govt. Printer, 1930.

Firth, M. J., *Native Orchids of Tasmania*. 1965.
Forestry and Timber Bureau, *Forest Trees of Australia*. Canberra, Department of the Interior, 2nd ed, 1962.
Francis, W. D., *Australian Rain-forest Trees*. Canberra, Forestry & Timber Bureau, 1951.

Galbraith, Jean, *Wildflowers of Victoria*. Melbourne, Colorgravure Publications, 2nd ed, 1967.
Gardner, C. A., *Wildflowers of Western Australia*. Perth, West Australian Newspapers Ltd, 1959.
Garnet, R. J., *The Vegetation of Wyperfield National Park*. Field Nat. Club of Vic., 1965.
Gray, C. E., *Victorian Native Orchids*. Vol. 1. Croydon, Longmans, 1966.

Harris, Thistle Y., *Wildflowers of Australia*. Sydney, Angus & Robertson, 1954.
Holliday, I. and Hill, R., *A Field Guide to Australian Trees*. Adelaide, Rigby, 1969.
Hosel, Jutta, *Wildflowers of South-East Australia*. Melbourne, Periwinkle Books, 1969.

Jacaranda Wildflower Guides. A series of pocket guidebooks published by Jacaranda Press, Brisbane.

Leigh, J. H., Mulham, W. E., *Pastoral Plants of the Riverine Plain*. 1965.

Meeuse, B. J. D., *The Story of Pollination*. New York, Ronald Press Company.
Millett, Mervyn, *Australian Eucalypts*. Melbourne, Periwinkle Books, 1969.
Morcombe, M. K., *Australia's National Parks*. Melbourne, Lansdowne Press, 1969.
Morcombe, M. K., *Australia's Western Wildflowers*. Perth, Landfall Press, 1968.
Morcombe, M. K., *Wild Australia*. Melbourne, Lansdowne Press, 1966.
Mullins, B. and Baglin, D., *Australian Wildflowers In Colour*. Sydney, A. H. and A. W. Reed, 1969.
Murray, K. G., *The Alpine Flowers of the Kosciusko State Park*. 1962.

Nicholls, W. A., *Orchids of Australia*. Melbourne, Georgian House, 1959.

Percival, M. S., *Floral Biology*. London, Pergamon Press.

Rosser, Celia, *Wildflowers of Victoria*. Brisbane, Jacaranda Press, 1967.

Webb, L. J. and others, *The Last of Lands*. Brisbane, Jacaranda Press, 1969.
Willis, J. H., *A Handbook to Plants in Victoria* Vol. 1. Melbourne, University Press, 1962.

ACKNOWLEDGMENTS

The author and publisher extend their thanks for the section dealing with collecting and preservation techniques which was prepared with the assistance of Dr John Child, M.A. (Oxon) and the staff of the National Herbarium of Victoria.

To the following people go sincere thanks for their help and encouragement in the preparation of this book: Gwen and Frank Baily (Manypeaks, WA); Sue and John Brudenall (Canberra, ACT); Mr and Mrs Curtis (Canungra, Qld); John Davey (Armadale, WA); Ian Edgar (Ardross, WA); Selwyn Everist (Queensland Herbarium); Neville Fenton (Dorrigo, NSW); Iris and Wal Fletcher (Kemp's Creek, NSW); Peter Judd (Gibraltar Range); Malc. Lewis (Armadale, WA); Betty and Wally McKenzie (Indooroopilly, Qld); Helen and Tom Milner (Darwin, NT); Roly Paine (Gibraltar Range, NSW); Bob Royce (Western Australian Herbarium); Pat and Peter Slater (Innisfail and Brisbane, Qld); Ann and Victor Urban (Alice Springs, NT).

The photographs that illustrate this book were taken on Agfacolor CT 18 film, using Plaubel Peko and Profia cameras.

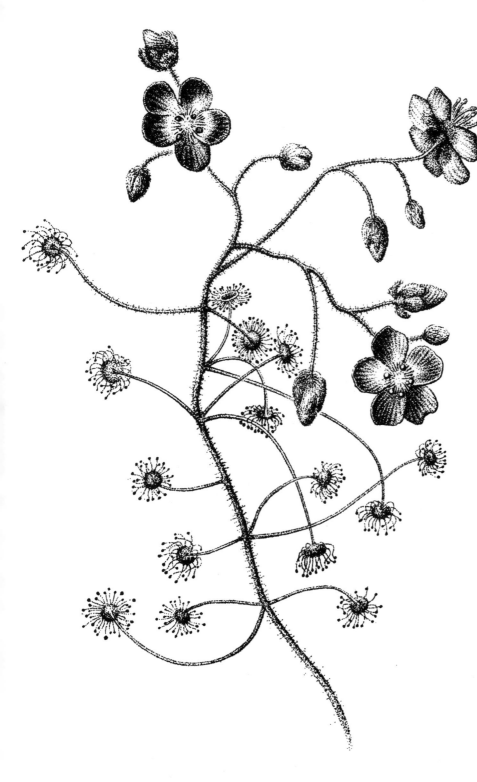

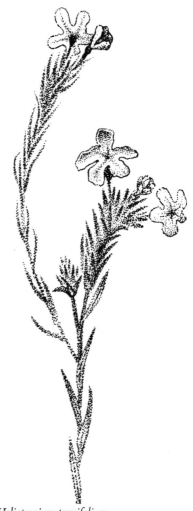

A Climbing Sundew *Drosera macrantha*
Colour: pink or white. Occurrence: south-west of WA. Flowering: Aug. to Oct.

Heliotropium tenuifolium
FAMILY Boraginaceae
Colour: white. Occurrence: 'top end' of NT, Kimberleys, WA. Flowering: Jan. to June.

INDEX

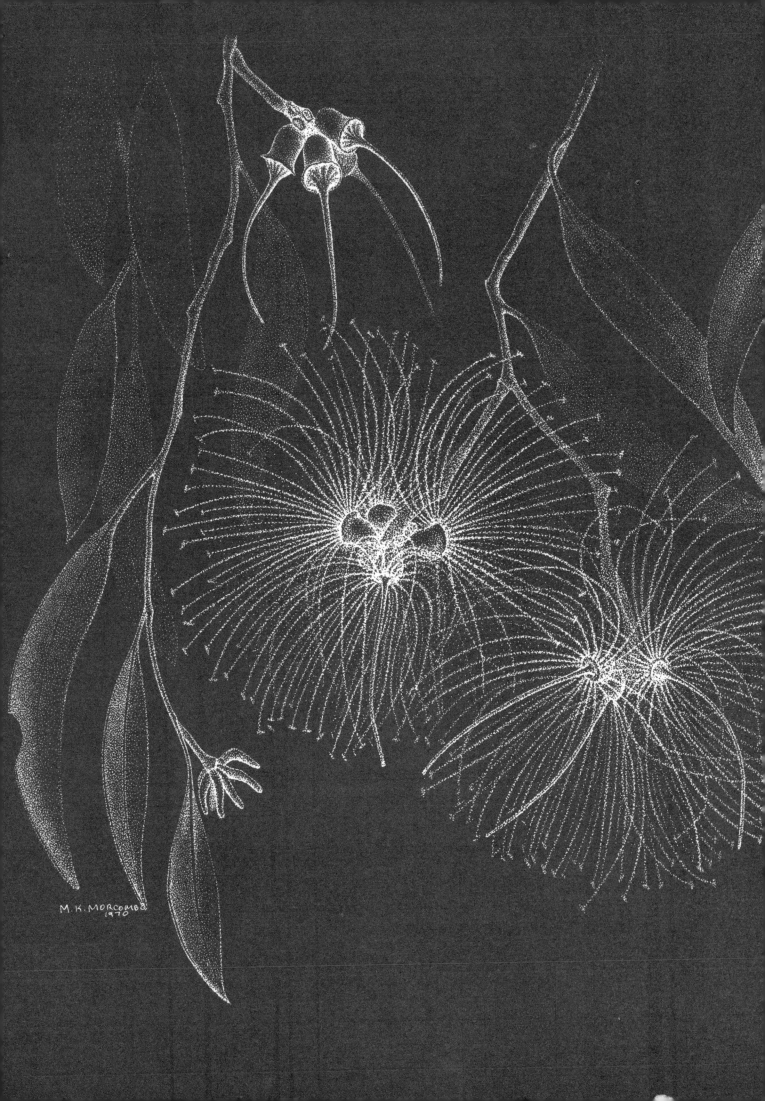

M.K. MORCOMBE
1970